TARGET VALUE DELIVERY

PRACTITIONER GUIDEBOOK
TO IMPLEMENTATION

CURRENT STATE 2016

Executive Editors: Kristin Hill, Katherine Copeland and Christian Pikel

LEAN CONSTRUCTION INSTITUTE

1400 North 14th Street, 12th Floor, Arlington, VA 22209 USA
www.leanconstruction.org

TARGET VALUE DELIVERY:
Practitioner Guidebook to Implementation Current State 2016

Contributors: See Page 145

Publishing Manager: Tonya Vinas

Designer: Megan Lasalla, MHL Designs

Printer: Signature Book Printing, www.sbpbooks.com

ISBN: 978-0-578-16842-5

Lean Construction Institute
Transforming Design and Construction

Lean Construction Institute
1400 North 14th St., 12th Floor
Arlington, VA 22209 USA

www.leanconstruction.org

CONTENTS

TARGET VALUE DELIVERY:
Practitioner Guidebook to Implementation Current State 2016

For History and Overview of TVD see above at Leanconstruction.org

INTRODUCTION

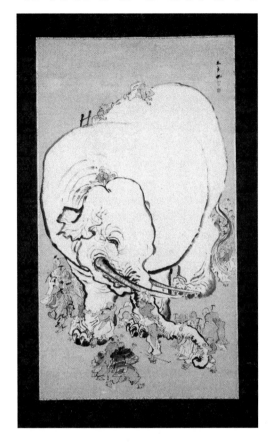

Figure 1: TVD is different things to different people

Source: Image used with permission from Wikipedia

Like the famous Indian proverb of the blind men each touching one part of an elephant and attempting to agree on a description, Target Value Delivery (TVD) can mean different things to different people. Specific tools and techniques used in parts of the process may be confused with the whole, and there has been a lack of available material to guide the actual practitioner in effectively implementing this valuable creative practice.

WHY TARGET VALUE DELIVERY INSTEAD OF TARGET VALUE DESIGN?

This book title uses Target Value Delivery because this is foundational to Lean Design and Construction project delivery. To say we only *design* to targets has the potential to propagate the division that has traditionally existed between the design and construction phases of a project. We have organized this manual to encompass all the phases of project delivery, each with a viewpoint of organizing the delivery method to achieving targets.

As the second volume in the Lean Construction Institute (LCI) Transforming Design and Construction series, this manual is intended to be a practical first step in creating a standard TVD framework. In addition, LCI now offers *Target Value Design: Introduction, Framework and Current Benchmark* to help teams understand the "what" and "why" of Target Value Design, just as this book is intended to describe the "how" of Target Value Delivery.

Many of the concepts relevant to TVD build on the initial volume: *Transforming Design and Construction – A Framework for Change* (Available at www.leanconstruction.org/about-us/publications/), and we recommend practitioners familiarize themselves with its contents to gain a general understanding of Lean Construction principles to support this deeper dive into TVD.

A Blending of Insights and Experience

This manual of practice emerged from a blending of the insights and experience of some 20 TVD practitioners who volunteered to participate in an intense, days-long exercise of collaboration and knowledge capture. The contributors were drawn from a broad cross-section of representatives of the Lean community: owners, designers, engineers, builders, and Lean consultant-coaches. No single subset of voices dominated as the group outlined, debated and agreed upon the structure and basic content. This output is meant to be a how-to guide to support TVD implementation on real-world projects. It is based on lessons learned by practitioners during actual projects in which teams steered design to targets.

Twenty TVD practitioners volunteered to participate in an intense, days-long exercise of collaboration and knowledge capture to create this manual. Image provided courtesy of Inside Out Consulting and Southland Industries

The contributors focused first on development of the business idea (Chapter 2: Business Case Planning) underlying the project, and systematically broadened the analysis to other aspects of project performance: from expanding and validating the business idea (Chapter 3: Validation) into a plan, implementation via design and construction (Chapter 4: Value Delivery: Steering to Targets in Design and Construction), and treating finally the occupancy of the facility itself (Chapter 5: Value Post Construction).

They then reached consensus of the core components required: Forming High-Performing Teams with a Lean Mindset (Chapter 6); Team Organization and Execution (Chapter 7); Big Room (Chapter 8); Project Planning (Chapter 9); Cost Modeling: Predicting Cost and Value (Chapter 10); Continuous Estimating (Chapter 11); Conceptual Design (Chapter 12); Production Design (Chapter 13); Construction (Chapter 14); and The Path Forward (Chapter 15).

Much thought went into the organization of this book and how best to explain TVD, which is composed of several overlapping phases. There are also multiple core components that are used across these phases. To provide clarity to the phases and core competencies, the team created this figure as part of the book development to organize the components of TVD and to guide practitioners as they work their way through this book. The columns define the different phases of TVD, and the rows provide a general indication as to when each component should begin and how long it will continue during the process.

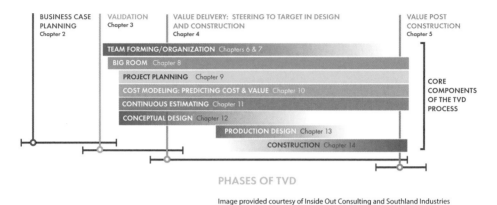

PHASES OF TVD

Image provided courtesy of Inside Out Consulting and Southland Industries

Figure 2: Target Value Delivery Overview

Holistic Application and Continuous Learning

Like any good operating system, TVD is intended to be applied holistically to obtain maximum value: All of the key players need to be engaged, and all of the major components and approaches applied fully; although it may be necessary to advance various pieces at different rates based on risk or need rather than the traditional 30%/60%/90% parameters.

HOLISTIC: Philosophy characterized by comprehension of the parts of something as intimately interconnected and explicable only by reference to the whole.

Although ideal, the use of Integrated Project Delivery Agreement (IPD) is not essential. Design teams using Design-Build and even Design-Bid-Build can make effective use of TVD as well, albeit with somewhat less effect than would be achieved in the typical IPD project, where owners, designers, builders, trades and others are most fully engaged from the outset.

We offer this manual to provide implementation help for TVD to the Lean community. In the spirit of continuous improvement, please let us hear from you with suggestions, comments and corrections. Lean techniques must continue to evolve if they are to keep pace with the ever-changing needs of Design and Construction, and your input is an important part of that ongoing evolution.

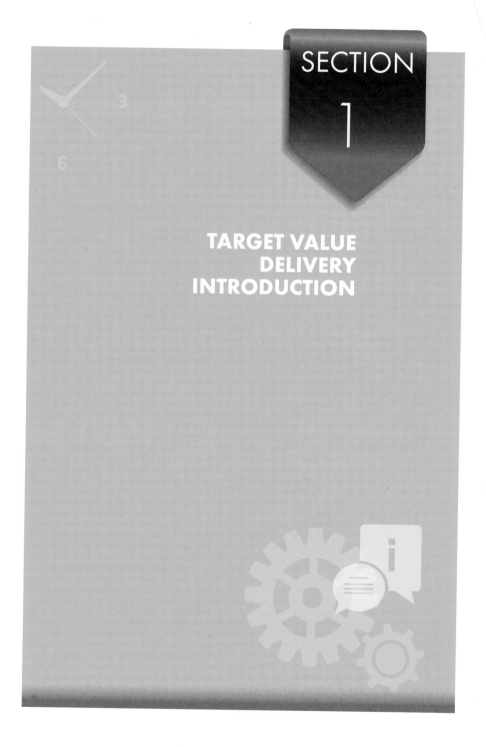

SECTION 1

TARGET VALUE
DELIVERY
INTRODUCTION

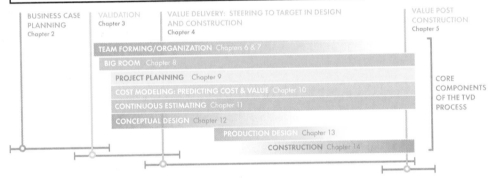

TARGET VALUE DELIVERY (TVD) OVERVIEW Chapter 1

| BUSINESS CASE PLANNING Chapter 2 | VALIDATION Chapter 3 | VALUE DELIVERY: STEERING TO TARGET IN DESIGN AND CONSTRUCTION Chapter 4 | VALUE POST CONSTRUCTION Chapter 5 |

TEAM FORMING/ORGANIZATION Chapters 6 & 7

BIG ROOM Chapter 8

PROJECT PLANNING Chapter 9

COST MODELING: PREDICTING COST & VALUE Chapter 10

CONTINUOUS ESTIMATING Chapter 11

CONCEPTUAL DESIGN Chapter 12

PRODUCTION DESIGN Chapter 13

CONSTRUCTION Chapter 14

CORE COMPONENTS OF THE TVD PROCESS

PHASES OF TVD

Image provided courtesy of Inside Out Consulting and Southland Industries

TARGET VALUE DELIVERY OVERVIEW

- Why Lean?

- Lean Design and Construction

- How Target Value Delivery is Different

Why Lean?

Construction industry studies have shown 50% or more of the effort required to deliver a built environment is non-value added effort,[1] or waste in the eyes of the customer.

The effectiveness of a labor hour has not improved in the last 50 years. Demographics and labor shifts have significantly reduced the construction industry's

[1] Construction Industry Institute Annual Report, 2004

labor availability, and the relative cost increases of the built environment are not satisfying the business needs of many of its customers.

Figure 3: 5 Cornerstones of Lean

The construction industry recognizes it needs to evolve to keep pace with the ever-growing complexity of the built environment, pre-manufactured alternative approaches and to make progress toward the same efficiency and technology gains other industry sectors have achieved over the last half century. Many believe and studies are beginning to show that Lean Design and Construction is a way forward for our industry.

Lean Design and Construction

Lean Design and Construction extends from the objectives of a Lean production system — to maximize value and minimize waste — capturing specific tools and techniques applied in a new project delivery method. Lean design and construction is a respect- and relationship-oriented production management-based approach to project delivery — a new and transformational way to design and build.

Lean production management revolutionized manufacturing design, supply, assembly and fulfillment. Applied to the design, supply and construction of a capital facility, Lean changes the way work is done throughout the project-delivery process.

Here's a way to think about the five cornerstones of Lean within a TVD project.

1. **Respect for people**

2. **Focus on customer-defined value**

3. **Delivering value and eliminating waste**

4. **Continuous improvement of processes**

5. **Shift thinking and behavior, supported with Lean tools to optimize the whole**

1. Respect for people

People transform ideas and materials into value. In TVD people are central to Lean project delivery. They must collaborate within and across teams using foundational Lean principles with the goal of optimizing overall value.

The production management-based approach of Lean project delivery encourages transparency and optimizes all processes and flows within design and construction.

2. Focus on customer-defined value

Through TVD, team members have the ability to understand and refine the definition of value from the customer's point of view, and this definition becomes increasingly clear through the life of the project.

TVD provides what might be termed an *iterative* value definition, as value is defined in big-picture terms and is then translated into details as the process continues. The project team seeking to optimize for the owner recognizes that this is an emergent understanding, not something simply locked in at the beginning of the project.

3. Delivering value while eliminating waste

Lean thinkers continuously ask, "Who is the customer of this process, and what do they value?" As what is of value is identified, Lean teams take action to eliminate steps and activities in their processes that use resources but do not add value.

4. Lean thinking demands a mindset of continuous improvement

Leaders must create an environment where experimentation is encouraged within project constraints and small, manageable failure is acceptable if the goal is to continuously improve. This atmosphere can drive innovation that will benefit the entire value stream. An overarching concept of Lean thinking is to optimize the project as a whole, sometimes at the expense of individual efforts. Lean tools promote the study of the overall outcome to determine where value is added or waste is included in each step, while constantly considering the value proposition.

Lean theory, principles and techniques, taken together, provide the foundation for a new form of project implementation. Building upon its roots in production management, Lean Design and Construction produces significant improvements.

5. Thinking and behavior (supported by Lean tools) to optimize the whole

Most conversation about Lean focuses on the use of Lean tools, which lead to tactical implementation of Lean approaches. Beneath the tools, however is a shift in how people and teams view processes. It requires that teams continuously learn, identify value and eliminate waste for the betterment of the overall project.

Some of the Lean tools discussed in this book (with examples and/or elaboration in the Appendices) are:

- **A3:** A one-page report prepared on a single 11-by-17-inch sheet of paper. See Page 159.

- **PDCA:** Stands for Plan-Do-Check-Act, a method of continuous improvement. See Page 163.

- **Pull:** A method of advancing the wherewithal necessary for work when the next-in-line customer is ready to use it. Pull releases work when the system is ready to use it. See Page 164.

How Target Value Delivery Is Different[2]

In TVD, a core team aligns around target conditions for delivering the project early on during business case development (Chapter 2: Business Case Planning) or at minimum during validation. The team continues to refine Target Cost[3], ROI or other owner-provided value drivers through the validation period (Chapter 3: Validation).

LCI defines Target Value Delivery as follows: "A disciplined management practice to be used throughout the project to assure the facility meets the operational needs and values of the users, is delivered within the allowable budget, and promotes innovation throughout the process to increase value and eliminate waste."

Figure 4: Driving Force of TVD

TVD is a very different model from the traditional, large-batch process of design, estimate cost and value engineering – a process replete with waste. Clients do not value the process of rework and loss of quality that comes from this traditional "value engineering" process. The driving force of TVD is to increase value while decreasing cost for all team members.

---

[2] *This section adapted from the Universal Health Services (UHS) Lean Project Delivery Guide, which may be found on the LCI website at: www.leanconstruction.org*

[3] *Target Cost is defined as the cost goal established by the delivery team as the "target for its design and delivery efforts. The Target Cost should be set at less than best-in-class past performance. The goal is to create a sense of necessity to drive innovation and waste reduction into the design and construction process. (Glossary, Transforming Design and Construction, op. cit.)*

TARGET VALUE DELIVERY (TVD) OVERVIEW Chapter 1

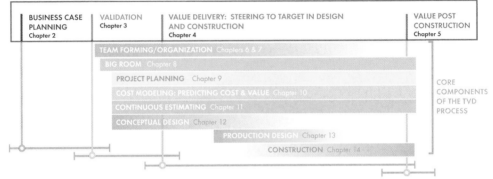

BUSINESS CASE PLANNING Chapter 2	VALIDATION Chapter 3	VALUE DELIVERY: STEERING TO TARGET IN DESIGN AND CONSTRUCTION Chapter 4	VALUE POST CONSTRUCTION Chapter 5

TEAM FORMING/ORGANIZATION Chapters 6 & 7
BIG ROOM Chapter 8
PROJECT PLANNING Chapter 9
COST MODELING: PREDICTING COST & VALUE Chapter 10
CONTINUOUS ESTIMATING Chapter 11
CONCEPTUAL DESIGN Chapter 12
PRODUCTION DESIGN Chapter 13
CONSTRUCTION Chapter 14

CORE COMPONENTS OF THE TVD PROCESS

PHASES OF TVD

Image provided courtesy of Inside Out Consulting and Southland Industries

16 TARGET VALUE DELIVERY: Practitioner Guidebook to Implementation Current State 2016

TARGET VALUE DELIVERY PHASES

TARGET VALUE DELIVERY (TVD) OVERVIEW Chapter 1

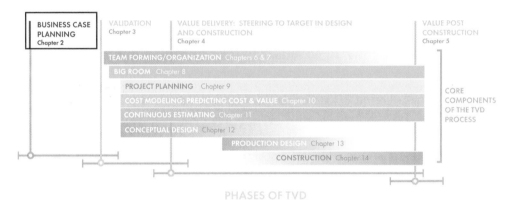

Image provided courtesy of Inside Out Consulting and Southland Industries

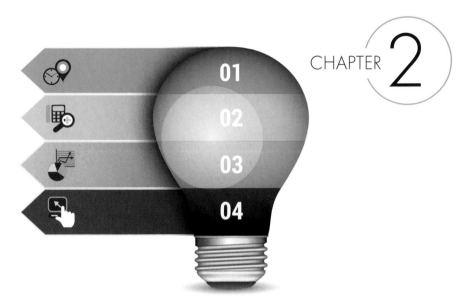

CHAPTER 2

BUSINESS CASE PLANNING

- What is the Business Case?

- Examples of Business Cases

- Key Element of the Business Case for the Project Team

What is the Business Case?

The business case is the operational use/benefit proposition described by the owner that initiates the development of the project.

This owner-provided purpose or "why" of the project becomes the anchor of project planning and execution; and it provides perspective for teams and key stakeholders to validate the project business case by going more in depth. (Validation is explained in Chapter 3.)

The business case is most effective when it is tied to an organizational strategic plan or high-level goal(s). It also could include a global (organizational level) statement of core values and mission, which the project team should study and keep visible as they creates more detailed project value statements and continue through the life of the project.

How owners create the business case will vary. Depending on the type of organization, the business case could arise from aspects such as:

- Market-needs analysis with a supporting business plan that describes anticipated market-capture potential and return-on-investment/ROI (for-profit organization).

- Availability of a development fund/endowment with global objectives for how that fund is to be used (not-for-profit organization).

In the Target Value Design Book, the authors explore the process of development of allowable cost as part of the business planning and they provide a useful flowchart for comparing allowable cost to market cost to help determine the viability of the project.

Examples of Business Cases

Ideally the business case will include all aspects of the project, including overall budgets, risks, expected outcomes and ROI, as well as any other factors that a particular owner deems important to their decision to move forward with the project. Owners need to do their best due-diligence in developing the business case examples. Underestimating what it will take to meet the "perceived outcome for the project" is a mistake that leads to rework, waste and frustration.

The business case also could be framed in a question form, such as: "Could we build X thing for Y money and have X thing available for use by Z date?"

Integrated Project Delivery

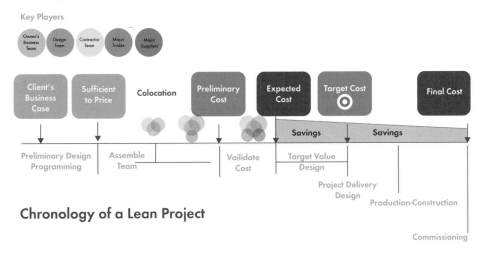

Chronology of a Lean Project

Figure 5: Integrated Project Delivery

Some business case examples are:

- Could we open a replacement hospital (similar to an existing hospital) in Castro Valley, Calif., for $300 million by early 2013?

- Could we find a way to increase overall visitor count by X% for $1 billion?

- Could we double the space for our church congregation for less than $5 million?

Some business cases will assume and require a capital project to be the answer to the question. Some will focus on an operational goal and will be open to a non-project solution, such as improving the human operational efficiency with no new capital project.

While business case methodologies will vary depending on organization type, generally this is the instrument by which the owner will make an investment decision as to funding the project, at least initially for validation. To this end, it is important that the owner provides the team with key factors and constraints, in objective terms, that begin to define the project.

Examples of these are:

- Minimum ROI

- Maximum capital outlay (could be constrained by financing, endowments, etc.)

- Schedule/Opening requirements

- Sustainability or energy-efficiency standards

- Factors affecting competitive advantage

- Other operational criteria

Key Element for the Project Team

The key element for the project team is to understand the owners' value proposition well enough that they can anchor the project values in it prior to moving forward with validation.

TARGET VALUE DELIVERY (TVD) OVERVIEW   Chapter 1

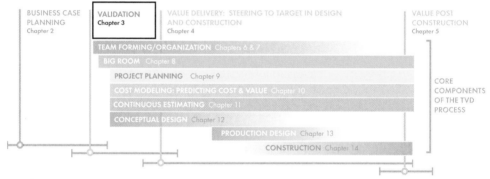

| BUSINESS CASE PLANNING
Chapter 2 | **VALIDATION**
Chapter 3 | VALUE DELIVERY: STEERING TO TARGET IN DESIGN AND CONSTRUCTION
Chapter 4 | VALUE POST CONSTRUCTION
Chapter 5 |

TEAM FORMING/ORGANIZATION Chapters 6 & 7

BIG ROOM Chapter 8

PROJECT PLANNING   Chapter 9

COST MODELING: PREDICTING COST & VALUE Chapter 10

CONTINUOUS ESTIMATING Chapter 11

CONCEPTUAL DESIGN Chapter 12

PRODUCTION DESIGN Chapter 13

CONSTRUCTION Chapter 14

CORE COMPONENTS OF THE TVD PROCESS

PHASES OF TVD

Image provided courtesy of Inside Out Consulting and Southland Industries

Figure 6: Value Statement courtesy of Penn State University and DPR Construction

VALIDATION

- Elements of Validation

- Value Definition and Conditions of Satisfaction (CoS)

- Steps for Documenting Value Definition

Purpose and Components of Validation

Validation is the phase where the project team (including the owner) begins to determine whether the project is viable and what a successful project would look like.

The project team should enter this phase with a clear understanding of the business case and expected outcomes for the project. The purpose of validation is to more fully vet the business case with the expected outcomes before the team continues with the project.

Ideally there is a pause with a go/no-go decision before continuing. Successful teams identify this as a project milestone and have a clear understanding that this is the phase they are in. When teams do not fully understand that they are in a validation phase, they often produce more than is needed or do not fully reveal what is critically important to make the go/no-go decision. They also presume they are in a complete move-forward mode.

The phase incorporates these components:

1. Teaming (Chapters 6 and 7)

2. Value definition (covered in this chapter)

3. Benchmarking and research of local code and site conditions; existing best practices; and lessons learned from prior projects

4. Conceptual Design (Chapter 12) sufficient enough to generate, analyze and vet big ideas for impact to value and cost

5. Cost Modeling (Chapter 10) to determine the expected cost of the project

Understanding the value definition supports the development of Conditions of Satisfaction (CoS) and a framework for building consensus and making decisions during the project.

Defining what constitutes value in the eyes of the owner is critical for aligning the project team's efforts with the owner's desired outcome; yet typically, value definition is not even recognized in the AEC industry, let alone regularly practiced. The intent within TVD is to create transparency and alignment around what the owner wants from the solution that the project team is going to create.

Value Definition

The value definition is composed of statements that describe expected outcome, or "value" that the project will deliver. Create a well-vetted, short, manageable list of values.

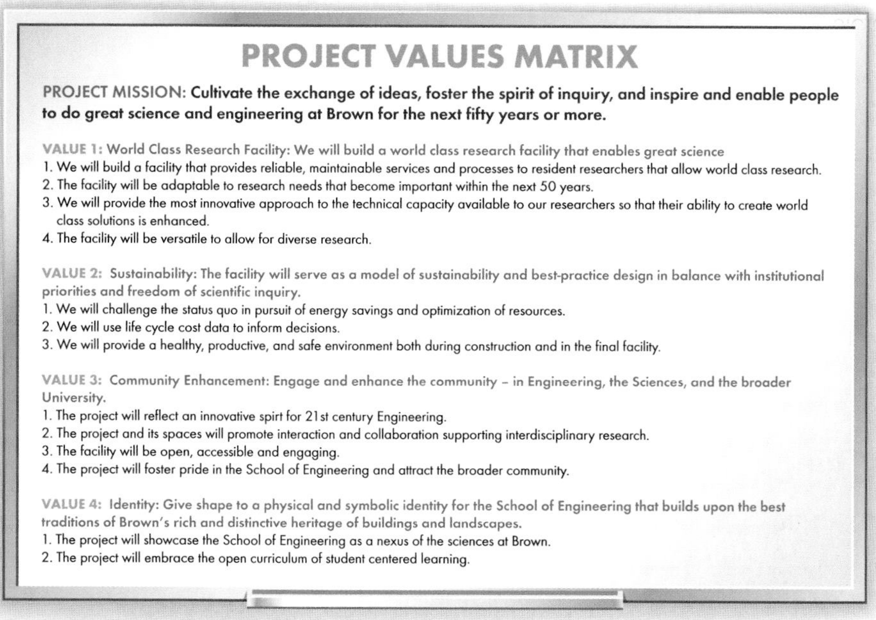

PROJECT VALUES MATRIX

PROJECT MISSION: **Cultivate the exchange of ideas, foster the spirit of inquiry, and inspire and enable people to do great science and engineering at Brown for the next fifty years or more.**

VALUE 1: World Class Research Facility: We will build a world class research facility that enables great science
1. We will build a facility that provides reliable, maintainable services and processes to resident researchers that allow world class research.
2. The facility will be adaptable to research needs that become important within the next 50 years.
3. We will provide the most innovative approach to the technical capacity available to our researchers so that their ability to create world class solutions is enhanced.
4. The facility will be versatile to allow for diverse research.

VALUE 2: Sustainability: The facility will serve as a model of sustainability and best-practice design in balance with institutional priorities and freedom of scientific inquiry.
1. We will challenge the status quo in pursuit of energy savings and optimization of resources.
2. We will use life cycle cost data to inform decisions.
3. We will provide a healthy, productive, and safe environment both during construction and in the final facility.

VALUE 3: Community Enhancement: Engage and enhance the community – in Engineering, the Sciences, and the broader University.
1. The project will reflect an innovative spirt for 21st century Engineering.
2. The project and its spaces will promote interaction and collaboration supporting interdisciplinary research.
3. The facility will be open, accessible and engaging.
4. The project will foster pride in the School of Engineering and attract the broader community.

VALUE 4: Identity: Give shape to a physical and symbolic identity for the School of Engineering that builds upon the best traditions of Brown's rich and distinctive heritage of buildings and landscapes.
1. The project will showcase the School of Engineering as a nexus of the sciences at Brown.
2. The project will embrace the open curriculum of student centered learning.

Image courtesy of Brown University and the Realignment Group

Figure 7: Sample values matrix from Brown University courtesy of Brown University and the ReAlignment Group

When a value is well described, it is easier – during the course of the project – to determine:

a. Whether the value is being achieved; and,

b. Whether the owner's perception of value changes over the life of the project.

Although the owner ultimately defines value, there are typically multiple customer groups within the owner's organization that have varying perceptions of value. In this case the value-definition process needs to drive at consensus among the customer groups, facilitated by strong project leaders in the owner organization.

Two key points to remember about value definition are:

1. Do not let the definition break down into describing solutions. Value should be defined at a high level. Solutions will be defined later by the project team and measured against the value.

For example:

Value statement: Brand recognition when customers drive by my facility.

Solution statement: I want a big sign by the freeway ramp.

2. It is best not to rank or apply weight to the preferences within the value definition. The project preferences should be held in tension by the team as each design solution set is evaluated to optimize around solutions that bring the most value overall.

As the team discovers what is of value, it might include things that are beyond the control of the team, but should still be understood and considered by the team.

4 Things That Influence Value

Think of the value definition in terms of four categories of influencing information:

1. Objective factors: Objective factors are fairly easy to calculate and measure, such as: a CFO says the company's internal rate of return on the project needs to be at least X%; or a campus administrator needs to house X number of incoming students.

2. Subjective factors: These human-focused factors typically are difficult but just as important to define numerically. Some examples:

    • We need winter shelter for all homeless residents of our city.

    • We want the lobby to have a "wow" factor and impress visitors to our new building.

    • We need space for visiting scholars that has quiet areas and IT connectivity to other universities.

3. Project constraints: These are the limits that define the boundary of the solution space for the possible design sets that could meet the Value Definition. Constraints can take the form of time (project schedule), money (project budget), technological complexity, environmental factors such as maximum building height, use of local resources or labor, sustainability (LEED Gold), etc.

These also can be operational constraints, such as: total staff to operate facility cannot exceed X; revenue generation must be net positive starting day one; the facility must recruit at least one neurologist with an international reputation within six months of opening or it will be closed.

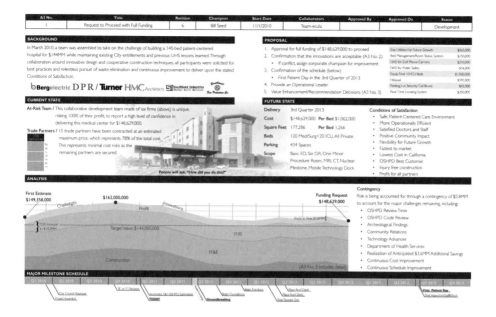

Figure 8: A3 to go to final funding. Courtesy UHS, Berg Electric DPR/Turner, HMC, Southland Industries, Southwest Fire Protective Company

VALUE OPTIMIZATION

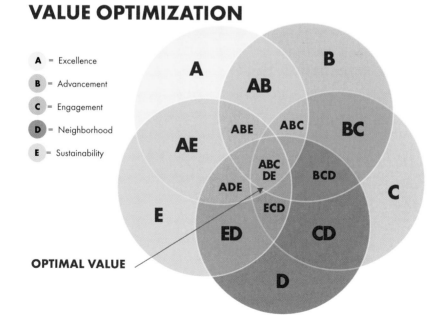

- **A** = Excellence
- **B** = Advancement
- **C** = Engagement
- **D** = Neighborhood
- **E** = Sustainability

Figure 9: Value optimization based on the value statement of the Penn State University project

4. Project preferences: These come as owner feedback that can be used to choose from among competing solutions. However, preferences are not value. Examples of preference statements are: a macro level "what kind of building in what location" or a solution-specific item, such as "under-floor ventilation or traditional forced-air ceiling ventilation."

Project preferences also can be operational criteria such as: lower cost is better; opening sooner is better; lower energy use is better. But they also can be operational drivers such as: the more efficient the staff can be the better; the lower the cost to maintain the facility the better.

Preferences often are expressed in a negative form stemming from bad experiences with specific solutions in the past. It's important for the team to analyze the root cause of problem-specific preferences to determine the underlying problem statement.

If the owner has not provided sufficient initial clarity to the value definition, the project team continues to work to achieve that clarity and consensus. Without this definition, the team risks making project decisions that are not anchored in the owners' value definition.

Expect that owner groups are not skilled at defining value, are not aligned internally on what value is, and that contradictory expectations are in play. There may also be disengaged or late-coming decision makers, which can cause a rework cycle to re-define value.

Conditions of Satisfaction (CoS)

The Value Definition output is important to inform the development of the Conditions of Satisfaction (CoS). The project team and the owner create the CoS after the Value Definition is created. The CoS are entirely within the control of the project team.

CoS are explicit descriptions by the owner of all the actual requirements that must be satisfied in order for the owner to feel that exactly what was wanted was delivered.

At the project level, they can be thought of as measurable statements that inform a project team about which tests a project must pass to be accepted as a success. They become the basis of decision making for the team and should be kept visible and referenced often during the project: in the design phase to inform cluster decision making, and in the construction phase to guide the process of making choices.

A well-defined statement of value and clear CoS are critical to enable the project team to anchor decisions and choose options that best optimize owner value. It is important that sufficient value analysis takes place during validation as this is the best opportunity to "invest" value into the project if it improves the long-term investment and is not previously constrained by a cost cap. Once a maximum allowable cost is set at the end of the validation phase, it becomes more challenging to engage in first cost versus long-term value optimization.

Guidelines for Developing Value Definition

1. Stakeholder identification

    a. Use the organizational knowledge of the project initiator to identify key decision makers at leadership level

    b. Conduct a brainstorming session with key decision makers to identify stakeholder groups and/or influencers

    c. If available, examine project retrospectives on end-user change-drivers to help facilitate discussion

    d. Create a responsibility matrix by compiling a list of all project stakeholders and categorizing on level of engagement, input and decision making

    e. Identify the key subject matter experts in the stakeholder group

    f. Identify the key decision makers in the stakeholder group

    g. If the distinction exists and is important, identify which decision makers have the power to say "yes'" and which have the power to say "no"

2. Value definition event

    a. Bring all of the above to a facilitated event to jointly uncover the value definition along with the team available at the time.

        i. The facilitator of this event plays a key role in the outcome. It could be a team member with significant prior experience in leading teams/customers through this process or a coach/consultant brought in to support the team.

        ii. The environment is another critical factor to the success of the event. Follow methodologies for Big Rooms (Chapter 8) and Open Space Technology to create a safe and productive space for brainstorming and creativity. Ensure an ample supply of markers, sticky notes and flip charts for participants to use.

b. If the project is inheriting organization values (for example a mission statement or a corporate statement of core values) review with the stakeholder group prior to beginning. It is important that the group considers consistency of project values with organizational values as these are developed.

c. Begin with a brainstorming session, potentially in smaller groups of stakeholders depending on room size, where participants write down value definition items in free form using sticky notes or flip charts.

d. Once these are collected, the facilitator leads the group through a process of grouping and organizing to stack similar statements.

e. With the initial list of value statements, the group will further divide the items to separate out those that are not values: constraints, preferences or solution sets. These still are important criteria and should be placed on a parking lot list for incorporating into the overall description.

f. With the final list of generated value ideas, the facilitator leads the group to consensus to arrive at a final list of those value items that will become the value definition for the project.

    i. Allow stakeholders to argue it out themselves. It is common to have contradictory preferences from different parts of the stakeholder group and to have to carefully facilitate the conversation so that they negotiate to point of agreement.

    ii. If there is gridlock, have a pre-determined tie-breaker (i.e., a project executive sponsor). It is important that this role is described to the group at the outset so there is added incentive to arrive at a consensus decision.

    iii. Tools such as Choosing By Advantages (CBA) may also support arriving at a group consensus; however, ensure that this is kept in a simple form as the stakeholders will not be likely to have time for significant research.

g. With a final consensus-driven list of defined values, the facilitator will review the work of the group, and the team will follow up with publishing the values in a format convenient for sharing as well as to use in the visual workspace.

h. At the conclusion of the value definition event(s) or in a follow-up session, the project team with key stakeholders will generate a list of Big Ideas that will then be evaluated to support each value, as well as formalize the project constraints and preferences that will be used to reduce the potential solutions sets.

Once the project team has alignment and understanding of the value definition and CoS, it is set to transition to actually validating the expected outcomes. The purpose of validation is to be able to set a clear enough vision of the project scope, cost, timeframe, etc., with a solid level of confidence that the project can be delivered within the expectations. This will involve commencing with many of the components described within this book, but with a constant eye to the expected outcome of the validation phase.

While often this phase starts to overlap with the next phase (value delivery), most teams find it highly beneficial to create a clearly defined milestone with expected outcomes. This supports the team understanding the level to which it should be developing information for decision-making purposes.

Typical expected outcomes of validation are having set a "target cost" or target that the team will now steer the project toward. There are different terms used for the target cost, but the key is that the scope, value definition and target cost are understood and that there is team alignment.

TARGET VALUE DELIVERY (TVD) OVERVIEW Chapter 1

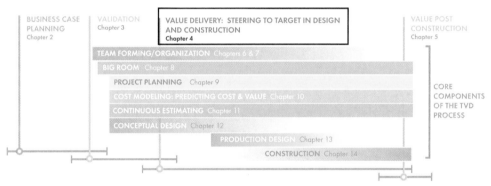

| BUSINESS CASE PLANNING Chapter 2 | VALIDATION Chapter 3 | VALUE DELIVERY: STEERING TO TARGET IN DESIGN AND CONSTRUCTION Chapter 4 | | VALUE POST CONSTRUCTION Chapter 5 |

TEAM FORMING/ORGANIZATION Chapters 6 & 7

BIG ROOM Chapter 8

PROJECT PLANNING Chapter 9

COST MODELING: PREDICTING COST & VALUE Chapter 10

CONTINUOUS ESTIMATING Chapter 11

CONCEPTUAL DESIGN Chapter 12

PRODUCTION DESIGN Chapter 13

CONSTRUCTION Chapter 14

CORE COMPONENTS OF THE TVD PROCESS

PHASES OF TVD

Image provided courtesy of Inside Out Consulting and Southland Industries

Figure 10: Monthly update on Temecula Valley Hospital for December 2012

VALUE DELIVERY: STEERING TO TARGET IN DESIGN AND CONSTRUCTION

- Adhering to the Value Definition and CoS

- How TVD Removes Wasteful Rework

- Releasing Work to Teams for Production

As the team transitions from validation to delivering value, it must have a clear understanding of value definition, cost model and target cost, Conditions of Satisfaction (CoS) and owner business case, including objective constraints. During validation, sufficient conceptual design decisions need to have been made, as this is the best opportunity to affect overall project value and cost impacts.

Adhering to the Value Definition and CoS

As work progresses in small batches toward intermediate milestones — many of which may be decision points — the design is continuously tracked and evaluated against the established values and cost model. Hand-offs of information or work product, decisions and outside input all drive the effort of the team toward realizing the established value.

Design of all projects requires continuous communication, collaboration and coordination by an integrated team. Without this, individual disciplines will develop uncoordinated, incongruous and often conflicting solutions in isolation — waiting to coordinate and reconcile these designs after a major project review milestone such as the traditional 30%/60%/90% check points.

How TVD Removes Wasteful Rework

In traditional projects it is common to uncover problems in the design and near the end of construction and so suddenly run late and over-budget; or there is suddenly a need to compromise the scope in order to appear to stay on time or on budget. The result is wasted time and effort in the form of design rework or "negative" design iteration, removal of valued scope, and ultimately field rework for issues not addressed or fully resolved during design.

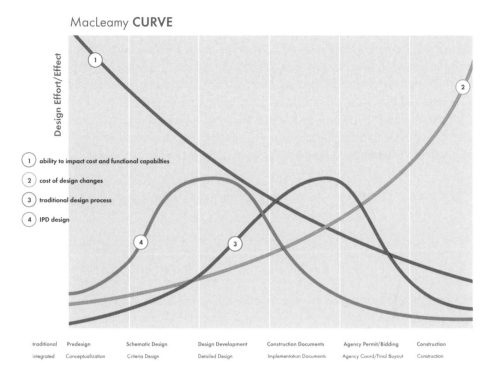

MacLeamy **CURVE**

Design Effort/Effect

1. ability to impact cost and functional capabilties
2. cost of design changes
3. traditional design process
4. IPD design

| traditional | Predesign | Schematic Design | Design Development | Construction Documents | Agency Permit/Bidding | Construction |
| integrated | Conceptualization | Criteria Design | Detailed Design | Implementation Documents | Agency Coord/Final Buyout | Construction |

Figure 11: MacLeamy Curve

Team operating systems and behaviors must be established to ensure this doesn't happen—that design is fully informed by and aligns with the CoS, values, cost model and project constraints—as well as being developed in unison by the integrated team.

This alignment is an ongoing process done through continuous cost modeling, not after-the-fact through a large milestone estimate and value-engineering cycle. This requires a conscious effort to create systems that track performance against each of the CoS.

....

Pull, See Page 164

....

Construction Pulling Design

The way in which the team plans to construct the building has a large impact on the amount of value delivered for the given budget and schedule, so the planning of how the building will be constructed should inform the design and how the design packages will be released. This is what is meant by "construction needs pulling what the teams deliver during design." This includes what is released, when it is released and how it is released. But even more importantly is to ensure that how the project is being designed supports how the team plans to construct it.

While design is acknowledged to be nonlinear, complex and iterative, Last Planner® System concepts can be applied effectively in the design phase to develop project-specific schedules that deliver value and minimize rework and waste. Once the project schedule framework is established, concept and production design proceed to deliver project value with timely stakeholder engagement maximizing windows for productive or "positive" design iteration.

Work transitions to construction as packages of work become ready. Shared project understanding helps eliminate wasted time and effort as the focus of the team shifts from designing to building.

In the Target Value Design: Introduction, Framework and Current Benchmark, Chapter 3, the authors explore Production Planning and Control and how the use of Last Planner® will steer construction to targets when coupled with reliable promising, measuring performance and learning from plan failures. These components are also developed further within Chapter 9 of this book, Project Planning.

TARGET VALUE DELIVERY (TVD) OVERVIEW   Chapter 1

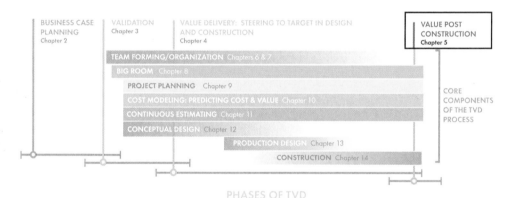

BUSINESS CASE
PLANNING
Chapter 2

VALIDATION
Chapter 3

VALUE DELIVERY: STEERING TO TARGET IN DESIGN
AND CONSTRUCTION
Chapter 4

VALUE POST
CONSTRUCTION
Chapter 5

TEAM FORMING/ORGANIZATION   Chapters 6 & 7

BIG ROOM   Chapter 8

PROJECT PLANNING   Chapter 9

COST MODELING: PREDICTING COST & VALUE   Chapter 10

CONTINUOUS ESTIMATING   Chapter 11

CONCEPTUAL DESIGN   Chapter 12

PRODUCTION DESIGN   Chapter 13

CONSTRUCTION   Chapter 14

CORE
COMPONENTS
OF THE TVD
PROCESS

PHASES OF TVD

Image provided courtesy of Inside Out Consulting and Southland Industries

CHAPTER 5

VALUE POST-CONSTRUCTION

- Why We Do It

- How the Owner Benefits

- Demonstrating Value in Capital Projects

For the owner, value is realized only after the facility is constructed and serving its intended purpose. This is the final phase of Target Value Delivery (TVD), when the Business Case and target values established during validation are reviewed for actual outcomes.

When the owner and team established project values (i.e., business case, value definition, Conditions of Satisfaction, etc.), they should have planned for how realization of these objectives would be measured. Those measures come into play now.

For example, target values for a new hospital might be patient outcomes via HCAHP scores, and staff satisfaction measured by turnover rates and ROI. Some target values could be harder to measure in the short term, and the owner should be prepared to track this value over several years, if not decades. For example, one value of a university campus project might be world-class facility for 50 years.

Why We Do It

Continuous improvement is a core tenet of Lean Construction and requires users to constantly test their assumptions and make adjustments based on results. The project team uses the PDCA cycle throughout the life of the project, but the Value Post-Construction phase provides the opportunity for the owner and key partners to apply PDCA from one project to the next.

PDCA: See Page 163

How the Owner Benefits

For owners and teams engaged with owners that build capital projects year after year, learning from one project to the next is critical to improving outcomes over time. Without taking time to determine whether it captured value from its project, the owner will not be able to continue organizational momentum to continuously improve for higher-value, lower-cost facilities in the future.

Author and leadership expert Jim Collins and his team found that an unquenchable thirst for progress is what allows organizations to move from good to great:

"Indeed, the drive for progress is never satisfied with the status quo, even when the status quo is working well. Like a persistent and incurable itch, the drive to progress in a highly visionary company can never be satisfied under any conditions even if the company succeeds enormously." [4]

[4] Collins & Porras, Built to Last, Harper Collins, New York (1994), pg. 84

Demonstrating Value in Capital Projects

Many organizations do not understand that capital projects are capable of contributing to the bottom line and so do not attribute responsibility to make a bottom-line contribution. Yet, TVD demonstrates how capital projects can reduce costs and further progress toward strategic goals, both of which contribute to the bottom line.

But doing so requires an organization to constantly monitor whether the project facility has served its intended purpose, having in fact returned more than 100% of the invested cost. This cannot be done effectively without measuring how well the value proposition has been realized and by learning important information to transfer to the next project teams.

Here is how to measure outcomes:

Retrospective: A structured reflective event resulting in common understanding of a team's experience.

1. Business outcomes

These outcomes determine how well the project has met the original business case and objectives of the owner. They are usually quantifiable by final cost of work, schedule performance and operational performance of the building, while meeting quality expectations.

For example, a hospital system may perceive a future demand for 250 additional patient beds. The business model has determined that it is worthwhile to build a new facility so long as the cost per bed does not exceed $1 million, and so long as the beds can be on line in 29 months. This type of retrospective is typically closely associated with the actual financials of the operation, and should be tracked over the course of several years to assure that operational costs like energy and maintenance/repair are captured in the overall financial mode.

2. Project process outcomes

The second measurement of project performance is "project process outcomes." In addition to on time and on budget, these include project quality, project safety and appropriate integration of stakeholder input. Time and budget constraints usually are set at the outset of the project by the contract. Quality standards normally are established by the owner and the project team in the development of the project.

Project process outcomes measurement is accomplished through a team retrospective event post project completion. Typically these take the form of a facilitated event with an outcome of a list of Keep-Start-Stop doing items and perhaps issues that the team has identified contributed to, or detracted from, the outcomes of the project.

3. Value outcomes

The third measurement of project performance is value. This step is completed through retrospective events, and in some cases direct measurement, over time after the facility is operational. This step will revisit the value-based decisions the team made throughout the TVD process and review how closely actual conditions reflect the assumptions and inputs that fed those decisions. The same documentation that was used in developing and communicating those decisions should be updated with relevant outcomes information, so as to benefit future projects.

Here, we are making a distinction between the various conditions so that projects will have business outcome objectives, project outcome objectives and values outcomes. It is important that those distinctions are met in crafting the initial "charter" for the project because each outcome is measured differently and performance of each has different consequences.

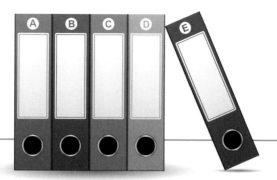

LEARNING LIBRARY

While project retrospectives and "lessons learned" are by no means a new development in the industry, an objective of the TVD process is to apply a higher standard of organization, measurable metrics and standardization in knowledge capture.

Another issue that has long plagued typical project lessons learned sessions is that of visibility. Too often these events take place and are documented in a book, booklet or memo that ends up buried in some project archive. There may be some benefit of the lessons learned by the participants (if they remember them on the next project), however there is little opportunity for institutional-level learning and knowledge sharing.

A key strategic engagement of the owner in the TVD process is to develop a dynamic learning library that is available to all current and future project stakeholders. By cataloging project decisions, innovations and outcome measurements in a searchable environment, continuous improvement across projects will increase exponentially.

TARGET VALUE DELIVERY (TVD) OVERVIEW Chapter 1

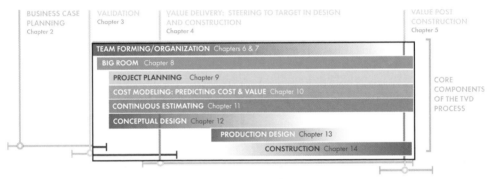

BUSINESS CASE
PLANNING
Chapter 2

VALIDATION
Chapter 3

VALUE DELIVERY: STEERING TO TARGET IN DESIGN
AND CONSTRUCTION
Chapter 4

VALUE POST
CONSTRUCTION
Chapter 5

TEAM FORMING/ORGANIZATION Chapters 6 & 7

BIG ROOM Chapter 8

PROJECT PLANNING Chapter 9

COST MODELING: PREDICTING COST & VALUE Chapter 10

CONTINUOUS ESTIMATING Chapter 11

CONCEPTUAL DESIGN Chapter 12

PRODUCTION DESIGN Chapter 13

CONSTRUCTION Chapter 14

CORE
COMPONENTS
OF THE TVD
PROCESS

PHASES OF TVD

Image provided courtesy of Inside Out Consulting and Southland Industries

SECTION

3

TARGET VALUE DELIVERY CORE COMPONENTS

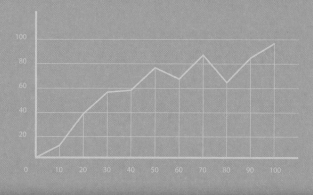

TARGET VALUE DELIVERY (TVD) OVERVIEW Chapter 1

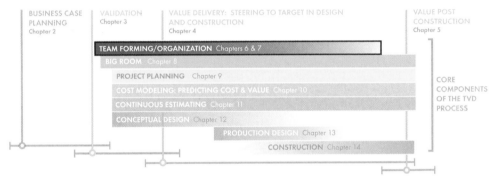

BUSINESS CASE
PLANNING
Chapter 2

VALIDATION
Chapter 3

VALUE DELIVERY: STEERING TO TARGET IN DESIGN
AND CONSTRUCTION
Chapter 4

VALUE POST
CONSTRUCTION
Chapter 5

TEAM FORMING/ORGANIZATION Chapters 6 & 7

BIG ROOM Chapter 8

PROJECT PLANNING Chapter 9

COST MODELING: PREDICTING COST & VALUE Chapter 10

CONTINUOUS ESTIMATING Chapter 11

CONCEPTUAL DESIGN Chapter 12

PRODUCTION DESIGN Chapter 13

CONSTRUCTION Chapter 14

CORE
COMPONENTS
OF THE TVD
PROCESS

PHASES OF TVD

Image provided courtesy of Inside Out Consulting and Southland Industries

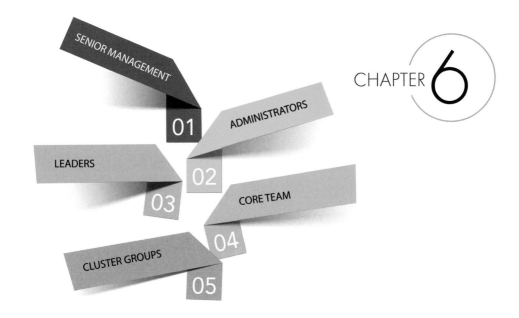

CHAPTER 6

FORMING HIGH-PERFORMING TEAMS WITH A LEAN MINDSET

- Forming Teams

- Keys to Team Collaboration

- Experienced Lean Partners (Big L Partners)

High-performing teams see results more quickly than traditional teams. Target Value Delivery (TVD) yields the best results within a high-performing team using a Lean mindset. Therefore, before we explore the TVD process components, let us learn how to build a team that understands and applies Lean principles and works together in a manner that will deliver results that meet the customer's Conditions of Satisfaction (CoS) and value definition.

Within the overall project team, there might be several sub-teams, such as the senior management team, core team and work clusters. (Team organization is detailed in Chapter 7.) The names given to these sub teams will vary based on different contracts that teams are using. For the purpose of this book, the terms are described herein.

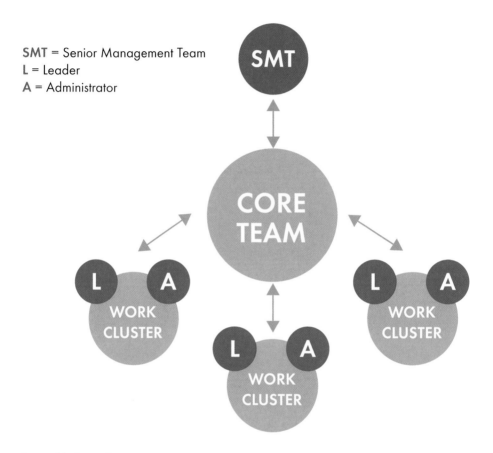

Figure 12: Team Organization

Forming Teams

Initially, the project team includes the owner developing a business case. However, best practice is to identify designers, builders and trade partners that will be particularly helpful in the reliable planning and delivery of the project as quickly as possible (once a business case is established) and engage them in validation. Typical trades often brought on during validation include: mechanical, electrical and plumbing; structural; site and drywall. This will form the basis of the core project team that will manage, plan, deliver and turn over the project.

As the first team member, the owner initiates and establishes the method by which the project team is created. In order to form a high-performing team more rapidly, team member selection should be focused on individual personnel and a commitment to the process and Lean construction at a company level. The experience of the people and company and their passion and enthusiasm for delivery using Lean approaches is one element predicting a high-performing team. However, team dynamics and interpersonal relations can affect this just as much. Selecting and developing high-performing teams is a skill set worthy of a separate book.

A good reference for this topic is the article, "What Google Learned From Its Quest to Build the Perfect Team." [5]

While understanding and alignment around commercial terms (i.e., the necessary overhead, profits and fees partners need to earn to have a successful project) is important, the critical selection criteria are centered on the talents and team-based factors of the individuals a company can bring to the table for a particular project. Understanding and building a sufficient skill set around these factors within individuals requires a commitment of time and energy on the part of the owner and any other team members already on board.

Lean project teams are organized differently than traditional project teams. The model promotes highly effective collaboration from disciplines, allows for more work to happen simultaneously, and dissolves traditional silos. This supports a sound, team-based decision-making process.

A3: Page 159

---

[5] Duhigg, Charles and James Graham, The New York Times Magazine, Feb. 25, 2016

Tools to support the selection process include:

- Pre-qualification proposal requests and proposals often prepared in an A3 format.

Partner Selection

Following are some sample interview questions to help select team members that will support the TVD process

TARGET VALUE DESIGN QUESTIONS:

1. What innovative processes can you bring to the Target Value Design process?

2. What lessons learned from other TVD projects can you bring to this project? Or what do think should TVD entail that it currently does not?

3. How can the design team better support the construction team in real-time estimating? What can/do you do to help the design team?

4. How do you inform the design team about the design process in order to add value?

5. What would your expectations be of other contributing partners that would be outside of the ILPD team?

6. What cost saving partnerships / measures can you bring to the team?

7. As change occurs, how do you communicate impacts of those changes to the team?

8. What is your definition of Target Value Design?

9. What is your perspective to staffing of estimating teams during the design process?

10. How strong are your conceptual estimating capabilities? Examples?

TEAM CHEMISTRY QUESTIONS:

1. What partner(s) (Owner, Architect, GC, Engineer, Fellow Trade, etc.) most affects your work (cost, complexity, conflicts, etc.)? How would you work differently with that party to improve the work flow on this project?

2. Describe your approach to conflict resolution for unforeseen project challenges that may arise.

3. What team building activities do you suggest to build team chemistry early in the project's life cycle?

4. When a member of the team is not performing, how do you encourage that team member?

5. In your past experience, what lesson's learned do you have to foster better relationships?

6. What do you look for to bolster chemistry within a team?

7. How comfortable are you in challenging other partners?

INNOVATION QUESTIONS:

1. How does your company approach breeding innovation within the company? Where have you innovated in recent projects?

2. What is an example of where you found waste in the design and/or construction process, and how did you resolve it?

a. What is your experience/willingness to sharing resources and purchasing bulk resources with other companies?

3. Suggest methods to drive on-time delivery of inputs and drive accountability.

4. Can your company provide previous examples and/or suggestions of innovation in design challenges?

5. How would you collaborate with other teams to drive efficiency? Please provide examples.

6. What are your estimating and scheduling capabilities and innovations?

WILLINGNESS TO LEARN, LEAD & FACILITATE QUESTIONS:

1. What kind of training or learning programs does your company participate in?

2. What ILPD and project tools do you see your team taking ownership of?

3. How does your company foster and encourage leadership within the team? (i.e. ICE Sessions)

4. How does your firm or company track burn rate (evaluate % complete, projected vs actual) and the quality of that completion throughout the project?

5. What should we/you/us stop or start doing?

6. Describe your experience with the Last Planner System? What are some pluses & deltas and new ideas you suggest that can make pull planning more affective on this project?

7. What is your experience/knowledge with Lean and production tracking?

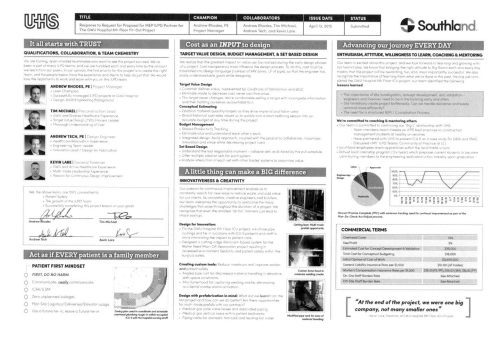

Figure 13: A3 for Team Building
Image courtesy of Southland Industries

- Company visits, project visits — especially when working with new individuals or markets. The value of visiting a candidate Last Planner®'s current project site, for example, can yield insight not otherwise obtainable.

- Reference inquiries with other customers, builders and vendors.

- The project team interview and selection of the strongest possible team member following Choosing By Advantages (CBA).

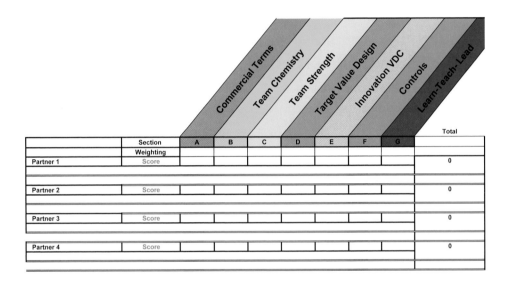

	Section	A	B	C	D	E	F	G	Total
	Weighting								
Partner 1	Score								0
Partner 2	Score								0
Partner 3	Score								0
Partner 4	Score								0

Figure 14: Partner Evaluation

Once the team selection process is initiated, and team members are added, it is critical for current team members (especially core team) to participate in the selection of subsequent additions. The intent is to create a self-selecting team dynamic, where the team itself has ownership of team creation and management.

Within the general project team, a core team includes representatives of each of the organizations steering the project towards targets and, in an IPD environment, sharing risks and rewards. The core team is considered to be the project management group and ultimately is responsible for ensuring 1) that the project team is implementing the TVD process effectively; 2) that the project CoS are being tracked and met; and 3) that all of the other sub teams within the project team are working as high-performing teams.

The core team is responsible for resolving issues that cannot be resolved by other groups on the project. Core team members must be able to communicate effectively, make reliable commitments, creatively solve problems, and put individual interests aside in order to do what is in the best interest of the project. They must also have the professional and technical experience to deliver the project.

Studies have shown that selection of the trade partners prior to completion of what is traditionally called a schematic design provides the best opportunity to affect the outcome of the project. In an optimized environment, the team would be in place during the validation phase and work together on the conceptual design concepts.

Keys to Team Collaboration

One of the keys to successful TVD implementation is highly effective collaborative practices among team members because it is this collaboration that creates value and drives work effort to meet or exceed targets while fulfilling the owner's CoS.

Two preliminary qualifications can help enhance collaboration. First, it is helpful to have team members with prior Lean and TVD experience to initiate and coordinate the process and onboard other team members. Second, teams selecting new members must do so based on expectations of new additions being beneficial to the chemistry, teamwork and dynamics of the existing team. If the team has limited Lean and collaborative-delivery experience, it should explore options to add that experience to the team in the form of a team member with experience or a Lean coach.

Experienced Lean Partners (Big L Partners)

A "Big L Partner" is a project leader who advocates for the Lean project-delivery process and is actively involved in training and mentoring team members.

There are also third-party Lean design and construction coaches who can be hired as facilitators. In any event, an experienced coach who can advise while remaining neutral throughout the process is an asset to the team.

As team members come on board, they participate in the process of selecting some or all of the future partners. This ensures chemistry on the team — another important ingredient for successful collaboration. Selection of the core team should align with key technical and professional experience necessary to deliver the project.

Much information is available on A3 thinking and process. For additional information on A3 a reference is A3 Thinking by Durward Sobek and Art Smalley.

Much information is available on Choosing by Advantages thinking and process.

The Choosing by Advantages Decisionmaking System
Book by Jim Suhr

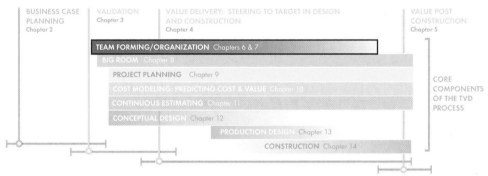

TARGET VALUE DELIVERY (TVD) OVERVIEW   Chapter 1

| BUSINESS CASE PLANNING Chapter 2 | VALIDATION Chapter 3 | VALUE DELIVERY: STEERING TO TARGET IN DESIGN AND CONSTRUCTION Chapter 4 | | VALUE POST CONSTRUCTION Chapter 5 |

TEAM FORMING/ORGANIZATION   Chapters 6 & 7

BIG ROOM   Chapter 8

PROJECT PLANNING   Chapter 9

COST MODELING: PREDICTING COST & VALUE   Chapter 10

CONTINUOUS ESTIMATING   Chapter 11

CONCEPTUAL DESIGN   Chapter 12

PRODUCTION DESIGN   Chapter 13

CONSTRUCTION   Chapter 14

CORE COMPONENTS OF THE TVD PROCESS

PHASES OF TVD

Image provided courtesy of Inside Out Consulting and Southland Industries

CHAPTER 7

TEAM ORGANIZATION AND EXECUTION

- How to Build a High-Performing Team

- Work Clusters

- Learning Simulations

Lean project teams are organized differently from traditional project teams. The Lean approach promotes highly effective collaboration among disciplines, allows for more work to happen simultaneously, and removes traditional silos between skill sets and roles. Such a team is a high-performing team, the level of team function required to drive increasing value and decreasing cost simultaneously through Target Value Delivery (TVD).

How to Build a High-Performing Team

Building a high-performing team typically involves the following steps. However, keep in mind that that steps may not always occur in this order, and will often repeat as the team evolves and learns:

STEP 1: **Create Team Organization Framework**

STEP 2: **Develop the Lean Mindset**

STEP 3: **Conduct a Kickoff Workshop**

STEP 4: **Select Remaining Key Members**

STEP 5: **Hold Onboarding Workshops**

STEP 6: **Create Operating Structure for Teams**

STEP 7: **Include Integration Events**

STEP 8: **Assess Team Health**

Step 1: Create Team Organization Framework

Once a project team has been formed and on-boarded, the process of developing the project team organization begins. With TVD projects, it is unlikely that one or even a few individuals can make all the necessary decisions associated with value, cost and schedule. A decision-making methodology needs to be established to facilitate execution of work and make decisions in a collaborative way measured against the value definition and CoS. This process includes the following:

- Core team

- Senior or executive stakeholders

- Work clusters and other project stakeholders

Core Team

The core team is composed of the day-to-day leadership for each of the major stakeholders associated with the project. In an Integrated Project Delivery (IPD) arrangement, any risk/reward-sharing member of the agreement should be party to the core team. If an IPD arrangement is not used, the owner should determine core team membership based on those parties who could most significantly inform design and constructability decisions. However, the core team should be small enough to work effectively.

The core team is responsible for the overall outcome of the project and managing other team-related needs:

- Ensuring work clusters form and anchor their recommendations in the CoS

- Fostering collaboration among work clusters

- Facilitating integration events

- Managing team health, learning and development

Also, in the event that work clusters cannot achieve consensus, the core team steps in to make that decision.

Senior or Executive Management Team

The senior management team is composed of the executive leadership of each of the major stakeholders associated with the project. While each project is different, typically the senior management will include a representative from the following: owner, designer, builder and key trades such as MEP, structural, and any other major trades that significantly influence the project outcomes.

The senior management team is responsible for:

- Coaching the core team and work cluster to help them resolve issues and stay focused on project CoS

- Resolving decisions and issues that cannot be made by consensus by the work clusters and core team

- The overall performance and health of the project team

- Supporting the project team in implementing Lean approaches

Work Clusters

Work cluster organization supports breaking down project complexity into an environment conducive to rapid learning and prototyping of solutions. Clusters share cross-functional knowledge for problem-solving and in the process begin to understand the ripple effect of collaborative decision making — better informed, well-timed decisions mean less iteration.

TVD benefits from the work cluster structure through its ability to focus decisions and actions on the project's value definition and CoS as opposed to self-interest. In TVD, no one person or company should design a solution alone, without representation from other project participants affected by the solution.

Work clusters should be formed as appropriate to the project needs. On smaller projects, the core team may be the majority of work cluster representation, while large projects will have more significant cluster management as described below.

Examples of work clusters include:

- Building system (MEP, skin, structure, site)

- Department type

- Discernible chunk of structure or scope

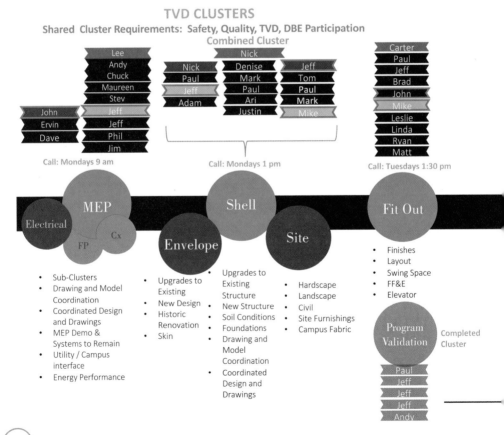

TARGET VALUE DELIVERY: Practitioner Guidebook to Implementation Current State 2016

- Big Ideas (See Chapter 10 on Conceptual Design)

- Specific project constraints or issues

- BIM

- Subject matter supporting the project values matrix and additional CoS the team has developed (environment, community, culture, etc.)

Work clusters must be multi-disciplinary, and must represent all stakeholders affected by a solution. Regardless of the companies and subject matters represented in the work cluster, TVD clusters must contain the following skillsets:

- Ability to facilitate Last Planner® System

- Understanding of A3 thinking and problem solving

RENEWAL

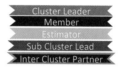

Figure 15: Sample Clusters

Image courtesy of Penn State University and DPR Construction.

SUPPORT CLUSTERS

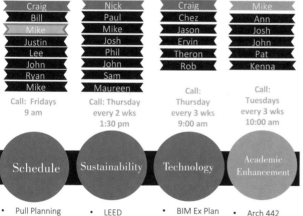

Schedule	Sustainability	Technology	Academic Enhancement
• Pull Planning	• LEED	• BIM Ex Plan	• Arch 442
• Site Logistics	• Energy	• Virtual	• ABE Student
• Staging	Efficiencies	Technology	Involvement
Off site	& Modeling	Application	• Grad and
Storage	• Tracking	• Model	Undergrad
• Pre-Fabrication	• Extended	management	Student
• Acceleration	Cx	• Innovation	involvement
• OT Impact		• PMIS	
Study		• Web Portal	

- Confirm Base Program Elements
- Shared Fermentation. Lab discussion

- Understanding of Choosing by Advantages (CBA)

- Design problem-solving capabilities

- Construction problem-solving capabilities

- Estimating expertise appropriate to the point in the project cycle

The size of the group should be manageable, yet accommodate a broad representation of stakeholders. Teams with high levels of trust allow one member to represent a multitude of stakeholders. This arrangement helps reduce cluster size.

Individual team members must be empowered to make decisions on behalf of their companies, scope of work or area of influence. They must also understand their boundaries of decision making to keep the teams right-sized. Each work cluster should have an estimator or person to report to the overall project budget, and be able to address the cost implications of decisions.

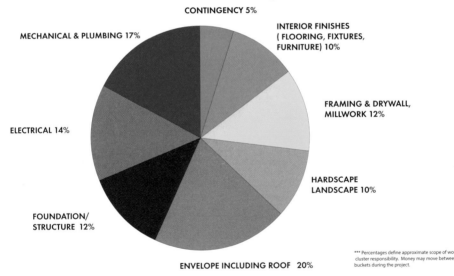

Figure 16: Work Clusters

TARGET VALUE DELIVERY: Practitioner Guidebook to Implementation Current State 2016

Responsibilities

Work clusters take a deep dive into their assigned challenges. In a TVD structure, they will respond to a particular budget goal as well as the CoS and schedule impact. The Project Milestone plan should inform the work clusters as to the challenges they should be addressing and by when.

This will ensure that the team makes decisions at the right time, and that the effect of those decisions on other work clusters and project team members is considered. A3 documents are an appropriate tool for defining who leads the charge of a particular topic and recording the date by when the decision needs to be made. The A3 also can inform the rest of the project team about what each work cluster is working on. All A3s should be accessible and visible to the project team.

A3: Page 159

Structure within the cluster group in a TVD environment is important to maintain the momentum of the group. Work clusters should have the following roles:

Cluster leader: The leader does not necessarily need to be the "expert" of the cluster subject. It is more important that the leader be able to facilitate and motivate the group, reference the vision and value set forth by the project, and serve as the report mechanism to the core team. This person needs to have strong facilitation skills.

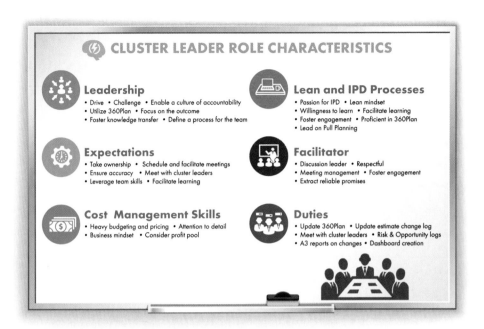

Figure 17: Cluster Leader Characteristics

Cluster administrator: It is important that the work done within the clusters is documented completely. This person(s) needs to respond to the cost model or other methods being implemented (See Chapter 11, Continuous Estimating.). They may be instrumental in ensuring that A3s move through a collaborative process.

Technical experts: Every work cluster will need subject matter experts responsible for the work being developed. Work clusters will evolve and may disband as a project progresses. Team members may change as the deliverables change. If there are no remaining deliverables outlined on the pull plan for the work cluster, then the cluster may have no further need to exist. If issues arise during the construction phase that need the expertise of multi-disciplinary team members, a work cluster may be formed (or re-formed) to deal with the situation.

Step 2: Developing the Lean Mindset

The lifeblood of any TVD project is an integrated project team. Moreover, TVD requires that this team have a collective Lean mindset. A Lean mindset is developed by self-learning and group learning during onboarding sessions (Step 3) and continually through the life of the project.

Many project teams are composed of people who have never worked together. They come from multiple organizations, different cultures and various parts of the country. They bring a diverse complexity of personalities, skills and experience. Characteristics of this team should grow to include:

- A strong foundation of trust among all team members;

- A strong team culture of respect that enables members to effectively work together and absorb and develop disparate ideas;

- A culture of encouragement that celebrates both small and large successes of the team and the individuals;

- An inclusive culture that breaks down traditional silos and barriers through collaboration, innovation and team achievement; and,

- A learning culture that includes reflections on lessons learned and incorporates enhanced processes into the project delivery model.

Onboarding, also known as organizational socialization, enables new representatives from contracting parties to quickly acquire the necessary knowledge, skills and behaviors to become effective team members. Involving team members in "learn-by-doing" activities is part of the onboarding process and:

- Immediately sets the tone for desired collaborative behaviors;

- Builds trust and camaraderie; and,

- Transfers ownership of TVD processes to all participants.

Onboarding is not a one-time event; it is a continuous process where concepts and culture are always reinforced, for current and new team members. The onboarding process is incorporated early on and consistently into the project life. Onboarding needs to evolve as the project progresses; and as information changes in the project, the onboarding needs to reflect that change.

Step 3: Conducting a Kickoff Workshop

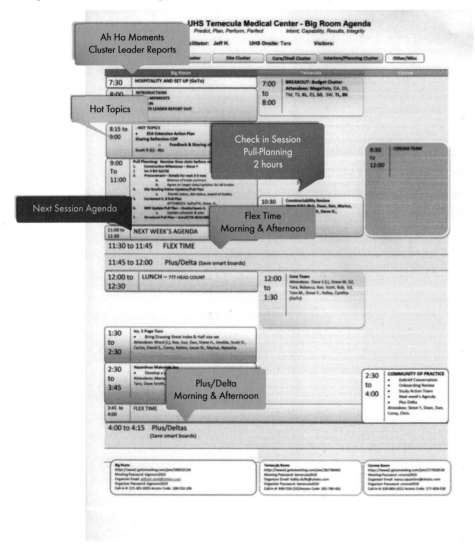

Figure 18: Big Room Agenda

The first step in building a Lean-thinking team is conducting a kickoff workshop or series of workshops to develop aligned Lean and collaborative understandings on the team. This may be the first time many team members are being exposed to Lean principles, and TVD necessitates team members have a firm grounding in Lean concepts, thinking and tools.

Tightly coupling learning with action is at the heart of effective development of project team capabilities. That means practicing concepts as they are learned and self-discovery through "Ah-ha" moments. Use of simulations and role playing is encouraged both to support the TVD process and build the team social structure (getting to know your team partners).

Kickoff workshop timing and duration are influenced by:

- The complexity of the project;

- The stage that the project team is formed;

- The depth of understanding of some foundational concepts by the team; and

- The geographical dispersion of the team.

The workshop should be scalable to the needs of the project and the budget for pre-project planning.

Suggested attendees for workshop: The focus of the workshop is on training and team building with those who will influence and develop the project. Consequently, invite key stakeholders, leaders, doers and planners who will actively support the project on a daily, weekly and monthly basis. That list includes:

- Executive leadership from all firms;

- Senior management team and core team;

- Implementation personnel responsible for project delivery;

- Owner and owner representatives;

- Operations and facilities directors; and

- End-user stakeholders

See page 167 in the Appendix for agendas for a typical three-day team kickoff session.

LEARNING SIMULATIONS

LCI advocates and makes available various simulation "games" and activities for understanding Lean construction, including:

- Airplane Game
- Pull Planning Blocks Game
- Silent Squares
- Tarp Game
- Dice Game
- Villego

A more complete list of simulations is provided in the LCI manual *Transforming Design and Construction: A Framework for Change.*

A kickoff agenda has several objectives:

i. Getting to know one another: The objective is to create relationships among team members and start to build a foundation of trust and shared experience.

ii. Developing how the team will work. The object is to build shared knowledge and buy-in to how the team will operate throughout the project based on shared learning, engagement and processes.

- **Create team rules of engagement:** How the team will function and support one another through communication, collaboration, respect, problem solving, decision making, identifying breakdowns, life/work balance and having fun.

- **Group exercises:** To highlight personalities, collaboration and being a team.

- **General learning topics:** Focus 90% of content for the session around topics that support the team in development and understanding of TVD.

- **Collaboration sessions:** Focus on developing team processes, strategies, and project CoS.

Each session should close with a call to action, identifying the follow-up steps, champions for each section, and finally a plus/delta for continuous improvement.

Step 4: Selecting Remaining Key Members

Once the current team goes through the onboarding workshop, it is time to determine and select the remaining key team members. The milestone plan should inform the team when additional members should be added. The team should determine the following:

- RFQ/RFP timeline

- Groups/batches of future partners, both near term and later

- Content and requested response format

- Interview process

- Selection criteria and evaluation process

Step 5: Holding Onboarding Workshops

Onboarding workshops with new partners should be planned and held at regular intervals throughout the project. A work cluster is often formed to take responsibility for the onboarding structure. All team members should be on boarded with the content scaled and tailored to the role of each team member.

Step 6: Create Operating Structures for Team

Some preliminary teaming strategies should be developed early on. These strategies vary for different projects so it is important that the team discuss what it thinks will work for its project environment. Often a work cluster is formed to address items such as:

i. A communications protocol

- What is the appropriate method of communication? When should face-to-face communication be used, and when should email, phone call and other virtual means of communication be used?

- How do team members share information?

- What technology platforms will be shared?

- What are the deliverables and what form do they take?

- What project information is readily available by dashboard to all team members?

- How are metrics developed and communicated to team members?

ii. A co-location strategy

- Will the team come together in a single space (normally called a Big Room) or will it meet virtually most of the time, or some combination of the two?

The scale and complexity of the project should drive decisions on co-location, but it is important to understand that real collaboration happens face-to-face, and we sacrifice some of the energy, creativity and humanity of the process by linking only through online meetings. Early in the project it is best to have more face-to-face collaboration as part of the team development. Once the project team has strong relationships, it is easier to use virtual meetings.

Strategies for using the Big Room can vary from a full-time co-location for the majority of the team on larger projects to a bi-weekly co-location event on smaller projects; or a hybrid version of some co-locations and some co-location events. (Big Room will be discussed in more depth in Chapter 8.)

Design a co-location strategy that best meets the needs of the project. Co-location is an investment of time and money, so it is critical that team members be able to support the co-location strategy, and that the owner understands the benefit of the impact of co-location on the overall outcome of the project.

iii. Milestone planning

What is the initial milestone plan for the entire program delivery? (See Chapter 9, Project Planning.) This will include milestones from the next upcoming milestone all the way through program occupancy.

iv. High-level clusters and members/skills needed

- Create a timeline (part of the milestone plan) and process for selecting trade partners.

- Start with firms that have the professional and technical competence to deliver the project, including technological compatibility required, and have the appropriate bandwidth required to meet project requirements.

- Then identify the people from the firm who embody the above characteristics required for the cluster team, as well as the professional, technical and soft skills needed and available for this job.

- Adapt or design the procurement process to fulfill the requirements to select the appropriate team members. This process will be repeated throughout the project as new trades are needed.

Step 7: Integration Event

Integration events should be part of the milestone planning for the overall project and should occur in the Big Room. The number and timing of the events is specific to the size, scope and speed of the project. Typically, they occur on a regular basis to maintain communication across work clusters and avoid unnecessary rework because work progressed too far without collaboration. It is common to schedule integration events weekly or biweekly. (See Chapter 9, Project Planning.) Continuously co-located teams should have integration events on a regular basis.

For an integration event to be successful, the entire team should understand what decision will be made at each integration event with enough time prior to an event for necessary pre-work to be completed therefore major decisions need to be represented on the milestone plan. The work clusters do the pre-work in the form of A3s and CBA analysis of alternatives so that they can provide recommendations to the larger group.

Decision Making Structure

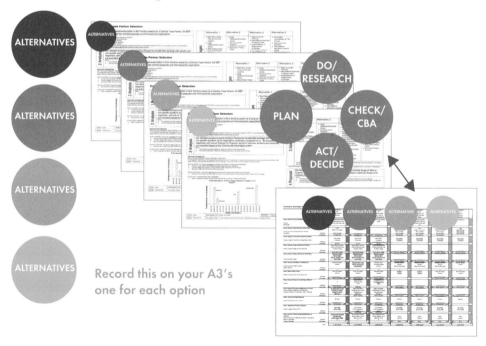

Figure 19: Decision-Making Structure. Example of A3 that incorporates comparison of multiple alternatives using Choosing by Advantages. Example courtesy of Sutter Health

LEGEND Underline Least Preferred Attribute per Factor Yellow cell = most important Advantage in Factor Blank = no advantage Circle = paramount advantage	Alternative 1 Structural Steel P & B- M.F. Non Bearing Walls w/metal Deck (A3 S6.1)		Alternative 2 Structural Steel P & B- M.F. Non Bearing Walls w/metal Deck (ConXtech) (A3 S6.1)		Alternative 3 Structural Steel P & B- B.F. Non Bearing Walls w/metal Deck (A3 S6.1)		Alternative 4 Structural Steel P & B- Shearwall- Bearing Walls w/metal Deck (A3 S6.1)	
1	*Factor:* **Sched (des, dtl, proc, fab, erect, fin)** *Criteria:* Want faster to enclosure (least # weeks)	15wk		12wk		13wk		15wk	
	Attribute *Advantage:* 2 weeks faster		85	5 weeks faster	100	4 weeks faster	95	2 weeks fastr	85
2	*Factor:* **Ease of standardizing fabrication** *Criteria:* Want ease of standardization (1hard-10easy) *Attribute:*	2		8		5		5	
	Advantage:			Easy to standardize	80	Somewhat easy to standardize	60	Somewhat easy to standardize	60
3	*Factor:* **Proprietary technology** *Criteria:* Want non-proprietary *Attribute:*	Not proprietary		proprietary		not proprietary		not proprietary	
	Advantage: Not proprietary		90			Not proprietary	90	not proprietary	90
4	*Factor:* **Local manufacturing/outreach** *Criteria:* Prefer system allows local *Attribute:*	Allows local		does not allow local		Allows local		Allows local	
	Advantage: Much more local sourcing	65				Much more local sourcing	65	Much more local sourcing	65
5	*Factor:* **Need for fireproofing** *Criteria:* Prefer no need *Attribute:*	Need fireproofing		Need fireproofing		Need fireproofing		Need fireproofing	
	Advantage:								
6	*Factor:* **Logistics feasiblity (delivery)** *Criteria:* Want easier *Attribute:*	Easy		Easy		Easy		precast walls can have shipping issues, titup erection can have issues	
	Advantage: Easiest		50	Easiest	50	Easiest	50	Very easy delivery logistics	35

Figure 20: An example of Choosing by Advantages, courtesy of Sutter Health

The goals of the integration events are:

- **Report-outs:**

  - Report on the work being done in each of the work clusters. The ideas being developed by the clusters should be reported with A3s and should include decision-making data that is focused on the value definition of the project.

  - These report-outs create an environment for shared learning and ensuring that the ideas being developed in one cluster do not have unanticipated consequences for work being done in another cluster.

  - Report-outs should have a structure and be relatively short in time, if done on a regular basis. Most teams allow 10-15 minutes for report-outs. If a cluster team needs more project team time, a separate agenda item should be identified ahead of time.

- **Planning:** Update the milestone plan and work cluster hand-off plan. (See Chapter 9, Project Planning.)

- **Cost-Model Tracking:** Update and report out regarding the budget and how the work being done by each work cluster is affecting the value, cost and schedule of the project. (See Chapter 10, Cost Modeling: Predicting Cost and Value.)

- Team health and on boarding strategies

At the close of an integration event, the project team should collaboratively develop the agenda for the next integration event and share what decision(s) that event will address. This will ensure that the team maintains focus between integration events. The agenda for events should be informed by the milestone plan.

Step 8: Assessing Team Health

After the team has organized and set the foundations for its team culture, it is important that members work to maintain the health of the culture. This prevents or minimizes team dysfunction and erosion in trust. A team health assessment is a tool used throughout the lifecycle of the project by many teams to take the pulse of the current state of project team. The assessment results should be used by facilitators to generate open, safe discussion among the team.

Team health assessments can take many different forms such as surveys, Big Room reflections, consensus on health, etc. The goal is to always focus on the current state of the team in an effort to continuously improve. The health assessment should include a look at the how the team is doing against its belief and values such as the level of trust on the team or how empowered do team members feel.

A method to assess the team health would be to ask the team members to rank on a scale of 1-5 how strongly they agree or disagree with some of the following statements:

a.   Communication between team member is open and honest.

b.   Concerns and problems are identified and addressed in a timely fashion.

c.   Team members treat each other with respect.

d.   Team members are empowered to change things are not working.

e.   Team members are focused on project success over individual success.

f.   The team celebrates individual/team successes.

g.   Team members actively pursue opportunities to support the project outside their traditional roles.

h.   Concerns are heard and addressed.

THIS IS A CRITICAL VALUE DRIVER AND IMPETUS FOR CHANGE; DON'T SHORT-CHANGE IT.

Critical to the viability of the survey is follow up, transparency and establishing a safe environment. First, the survey results need to be shared with the team. Second, the team needs to focus on addressing issues identified in the survey. Finally, team tools and team trust need to be monitored over time and countermeasures taken where it appears that trust is declining.

PDCA: See Page 163

The project leadership team needs to fully support the steps developed by the team to better implement process or to increase collaboration and trust on the job. Where gaps between ideal state and the current state have been identified, teams can use the PDCA method to address the culture gap.

Beliefs and Values

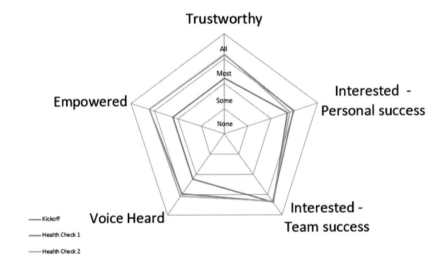

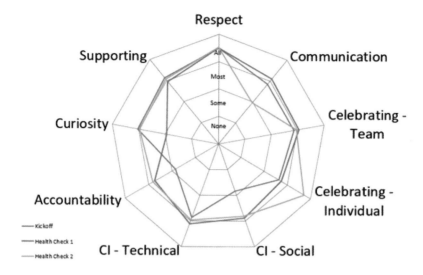

Figure 21: Samples of Team Health Assessment report out. The different line colors represent survey's taken at different point during the life of the project. Images used courtesy of Southland Industries

TARGET VALUE DELIVERY (TVD) OVERVIEW Chapter 1

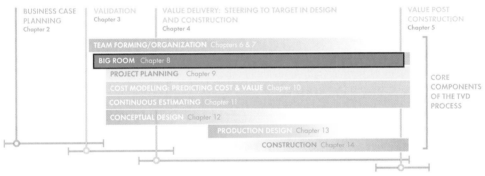

BUSINESS CASE
PLANNING
Chapter 2

VALIDATION
Chapter 3

VALUE DELIVERY: STEERING TO TARGET IN DESIGN
AND CONSTRUCTION
Chapter 4

VALUE POST
CONSTRUCTION
Chapter 5

TEAM FORMING/ORGANIZATION Chapters 6 & 7

BIG ROOM Chapter 8

PROJECT PLANNING Chapter 9

COST MODELING: PREDICTING COST & VALUE Chapter 10

CONTINUOUS ESTIMATING Chapter 11

CONCEPTUAL DESIGN Chapter 12

PRODUCTION DESIGN Chapter 13

CONSTRUCTION Chapter 14

CORE
COMPONENTS
OF THE TVD
PROCESS

PHASES OF TVD

Image provided courtesy of Inside Out Consulting and Southland Industries

Example of Big Room at Stanford Hospital, courtesy of the ReAlignment Group

BIG ROOM

- What is a Big Room?

- How to Set Up a Big Room

- What Happens in a Big Room

What is a Big Room?

A Big Room is an approach used to facilitate Lean principles in design and construction. It is a space that physically brings together designers, builders and facility operators to work collaboratively. An effective Big Room also supports cross-functional team collaboration by advancing work and bringing teams involved on a project up to speed on the activities of other groups or individuals.

Figure 22: Visual work displays in a Big Room.

The Big Room also provides teams with time to discuss project-wide concerns such as budgets, hot topics or global changes. Designing and forming a Big Room requires a significant investment of time and money; however, this investment adds value to the project and drives down overall project costs.

Benefits and Purpose

A Big Room aims to improve collaboration through greater team interaction. Teams are able to deliver a "higher-performing building" on time and on budget; and team members support each other more effectively and align themselves with the goals of the project. Co-location makes it easier to ask team members for information, resulting in less waste, breakdown of the "silo mentality" within the project and rapid advancement of work in a short period of time.

It also is important to remember that the Big Room is more than co-location of people: It is about collaborative behavior and the work it produces. A Big Room is designed to support cross-functional and high-performing teams in advancing workflow.

For a Big Room to be effective, certain rules need to be established. Some of these include:

- Participants must come prepared to be able to advance work while in the Big Room.

- There must be a focus on improving the process

- There should be effective onboarding at the beginning of the project and when new members join the team.

- Positive reinforcement should be encouraged.

- There should be a focus on learning, coaching and mentoring.

- This is a safe zone. Everyone is encouraged to speak their mind without concern for embarrassment or ridicule by others.

- No stripes. We all have equal status and have a say in all matters; no one person has more authority than another.

- Speak up. Get engaged in the conversation and share ideas; your opinion is important in helping guide the team.

- Listen to others. Focusing on what others have to say helps you understand their point of view.

High-Performance Teams

The project team is critical to establishing an effective Big Room environment. High-performing teams see results more quickly than traditional teams. The team is the "lifeblood and foundation" of an effective and efficient Lean project. The challenge of many projects is that this team is temporary and needs to be able to perform at a high level relatively quickly. For this reason, it is important to quickly create a high-performing team so that it can make the required changes in order to deliver outstanding results. More on high performance teams may be found in Chapter 6.

Big Room Implementation: When?

The behaviors and activities of the Big Room environment should begin as early in the project as possible, even if the whole team is not yet formed. The frequency of Big Room sessions varies from project to project and within different phases of the project; however, the frequency must support the work at hand and any project commitments and/or goals. The team must therefore continuously determine the right frequency and duration of sessions. For example, a half-day per week may be appropriate for a very small project, and a complete co-location might be suitable for larger projects.

Over the course of the project, the key participants in the Big Room should and will change according to the type of work being produced and the makeup of team members who add value to each phase of the project. It is important that the team include the right people at the right time. Along with smaller monthly changes, the entire nature of the Big Room could change several times throughout the life of the project.

Setting up a Big Room

The Big Room is about fostering behaviors that lead to high levels of collaboration, and thus to high-performing teams. While this is a significant investment of time and money, when conducted well, it adds value to the overall project and will drive down the total project cost. Teams rapidly advance work in a relatively short amount of time with less rework due to the fact that they have the collective brainpower in the room working together. Considerations for the physical space of the Big Room include:

- Large open room
- Break out spaces/rooms
- Technology to support team's activities:
  - Smartboards
  - Video conferencing
  - White boards
  - Internet and companies' connectivity
- File- and information-sharing structure
- Bio considerations: restrooms, kitchen
- Visuals: sticky notes, markers, flip charts

Each Big Room is different. The above are guidelines for consideration as you structure a Big Room to best meet your needs.

Venues

There are three types of Big Room venues:

- Co-located, where participants are continuously located together with continuous collaboration.
- Recurring; where participants meet in person on a regular schedule and recurring basis however, they are not co-located.
- Hybrid, which is a combination of in-person and virtual attendance by select participants.

The Agenda

An agenda determines the intentions for a Big Room session. It identifies the expected outcomes to advance the work, determines the necessary participants, and provides a timeline for the length of the meeting. An agenda should be prepared for all sessions, both because it promotes team efficiency and communicates respect for team members' time and the value they add to the project.

Preparing an agenda should be done collaboratively with all team members. You want to determine the frequency of the Big Room sessions, as well as the breakout sessions, which arise from the Pull Plan. Preparing the agenda should happen at the end of a recurring session for the next session.

Remember to publish or post the agenda well before the session to allow participants to prepare for the meeting. A typical agenda could include some or all of the following:

1. "Ah-ha" moments
2. Hot topics and top concerns
3. Team health assessment
4. Check-in session
5. Pull Plan
6. Cluster leader reports
7. Next session agenda
8. Flex time /make-up time
9. Learning or team-building
10. Plus/delta

Examples of activities in a Big Room Session

Always begin the Big Room session with introductions. Have each participant state their name, their role on the project and one thing about them (i.e., favorite movie, first car and how it met its demise, favorite sports team, favorite movie star, etc.).

- Project planning
- Learning
- Team-building
- Collaborative problem solving
- Cost model tracking
- Decision making
- PDCA

TARGET VALUE DELIVERY (TVD) OVERVIEW Chapter 1

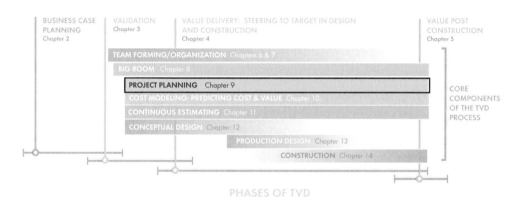

Image provided courtesy of Inside Out Consulting and Southland Industries

CHAPTER 9

Planning wall at UHS Temecula

PROJECT PLANNING

- Milestone Planning Best Practices

- Traditional Planning Vs. TVD

- Work Structure and Design Packaging

- Principles for Effective Design Planning

In the traditional project-planning environment, a few select individuals (the project planners) work diligently to integrate dozens of discrete schedules from all of the designers, builders and owner parties. Restricted by traditional workflows and contracts, the parties are kept separate, generally providing input to the project team through their respective planner or even keeping their own schedules.

5 - CONNECTED CONVERSATIONS

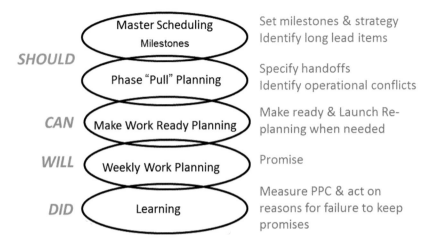

Figure 23: Last Planner® System

The traditional approach misses the key opportunity afforded by the Last Planner® System (LPS), which is to engage all parties in direct conversation with each other. It is through these collaborative conversations that the project team captures the wisdom and experience of dozens of parties and applies it to test, refine and improve the unified project schedule; as well as by identifying major incongruities or disconnects among the multiple schedules, false assumptions and opportunities for innovation. Through LPS, understanding shifts from a few key planners to dozens or even hundreds of project participants and the quality and reliability of the project schedule improves by leaps and bounds.

Milestone Planning

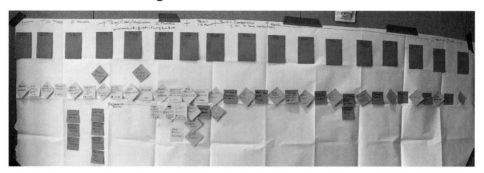

Figure 24: Milestone Planning

LPS starts with developing a collaborative milestone plan.

A milestone is an action or event marking a significant change or stage in development of the project, releasing a next significant phase of work. A series of milestones/events become building blocks for development of an overall project schedule.

Milestone planning is a process of identifying key interactions, relationships, decisions and deliverables required to release subsequent phases of a program into a high-level program milestone plan.

Teams that skip milestone planning risk producing deliverables with flawed or incomplete decision making and uncoordinated design, both of which lead to rework and negative iteration. Team ownership of the milestone plan and schedule goal commitments is very important to the success of the project.

The collaborative planning process focuses on handoffs between parties. These handoffs are the most important milestones to plan; however, they often receive the least attention because they are the most challenging to understand and typically face-to-face planning events bring understanding to the necessary level.

Such in-person events might seem too burdensome for a team that is perpetually busy trying to execute the work, but this false logic leads many teams to conclude: We don't have time to plan—yet they expend orders of much more effort on wasteful activities not generating value as defined by the project.

Figure 25: Pull planning for the Design Phase of Sharp Chula Vista Emergency Department Photo courtesy of The ReAlignment Group and Southland Industries.

Milestone Planning Best Practices

Milestone planning in a Target Value Delivery (TVD) project provides teams with an understanding of how the program is performing and meeting key deliverables.

Milestones mark key points at starting/ending of an activity, i.e., the need for internal/external review or budget checks. It is essential to align understanding of the project team around the project time constraints, key hand-offs and concurrent work.

The key to making this process meaningful is to dig beneath the surface of traditional project phases or milestones (i.e., schematic, 30/60/90%) to uncover the critical construction needs, project decision points, and design handoffs that, left unplanned, can put the entire project at risk.

Do it early: Milestone planning should be done as early as possible in the project, so durations in many cases are going to be estimates. Similar to conceptual estimating, this is "conceptual planning" to provide a framework.

Big Room, Page 159

Pick the right location: Milestone planning should be a collaborative event conducted in a neutral location, i.e., Big Room, such that participants can be focused and engaged in the process. A facilitator/time keeper is a crucial role in facilitating the process of mapping (placement of milestone sticky notes) on the program timeline. (You will need a large space, sized for the number of participants with adequate wall space to place the program timeline.)

Match timeline to project scope: The timeline will be defined to the level (year/month/week/day) as needed for the size and complexity of the program. The customers/stakeholders will need to be identified. Typical participants include owner, designers, builders, key trades, AHJ, subject matter experts (SMEs) – for each of the following categories:

- Plan permit (Project Development Plan)

  - Community/municipality/county/state/country requirements

  - Land acquisition

- Regulatory agencies and communication plan

- Environmental permitting (air/waste water effluent and current limits)

- Procurement plan

  - Contracting suppliers – commercial analysis

  - Material procurement

  - Equipment procurement

- Resource plan/organizations

- Schedule plan (overall program/project(s) schedule)

- Funding plan

- Estimating plan

- Program logistics

- Construction site logistics plan

  - Construction site security plan

- Entitlements

- Design package strategy delivering value in design

- Construction execution plan and sequencing delivering value in construction

- Quality/commissioning plan

- Acceptance/turnover plan

- Occupancy plan

Traditional Planning vs. TVD

In a more traditional approach of working toward major design review cycles (30%, 60%) or generic deliverable milestones such as schematic design and design development, teams work to produce uncoordinated or incomplete work with the intent to coordinate and validate this work against the schedule and budget at this milestone in a single large batch of work.

This is wasteful in terms of soft cost and the project time it takes to produce and review these documents. Using a TVD approach, the team focuses on planning decisions and handoffs, ongoing coordination, and integration events prioritized by project need. The team produces design documents only for a specific purpose, when an activity is complete or nearly complete. The deliverables are simply a record of timely, coordinated and sound decision-making that has already occurred.

Project team members may bring decades of expertise and experience in traditional delivery methods to a project. For effective planning of the design process to bring value, the planning facilitator asks these team members to set aside expertise in traditional design deliverable paradigms for the moment, and instead leverages that expertise and experience to identify and uncover the key project drivers in terms of decisions, handoffs, work-packaging strategies; and the related activities behind the deliverables.

Instead of planning a 30% review milestone for a building, plan all the decisions, deliverables and activities to release the foundations, or the first floor of steel. Be specific, and start in small chunks of scope. Ask the team members to bring their top five needs to the first planning session to get the conversation started.

Phase plans can be developed that identify interim design review milestones for estimating, coordination, decision-points or leadership review. As projects move toward an integrated culture — with co-located teams, and near-real-time sharing of design information — formal design review milestones become less important.

Figure 26: Creating Flow

Here's an example:

A project team may share structural steel design models on an ongoing basis, for coordination and review by their work cluster at any time. These models may be presented or reviewed at large integration events with the broader team. These same models are delivered directly to the detailer, where it is further developed, and sent to fabrication. Drawings are produced only for a specific purpose or need, in this case permitting. The team decides to hold one "final review" of the 2D documents to assure quality and coordination of the 2D representation.

The Lean leader or planning facilitator may ask these questions of the team, continuing to test and refine the plan in each session:

- How is the work structured? (What is the packaging strategy?)

- How does the packaging strategy bring project value?

- When do the work packages need to be released to support permitting, procurement, fabrication or installation?

- What project decisions need to be made and when, to support the packaging strategy and minimize rework?

- Where decisions are not possible, what flexible accommodations can be made?

- Can we design to an envelope (weight, space, area, conduit, etc.), paying for flexibility in the interest of a higher schedule priority to release the work?

- What does each design group need from the others to support the completion of their work packages? Ask each group to bring its "top five" to get things rolling.

- Do the design handoffs align? Are some groups pulling ahead or falling behind others?

- What are the handoffs to construction? Have they been fully vetted, tested and calibrated against all current project knowledge?

Understanding Pull Planning

The process brings the various stakeholder parties together to develop an integrated plan that provides alignment of program participants and understanding of the interaction among program participants.

The process uses Pull Planning, which is a Lean tool and part of the Last Planner® System (LPS). The intention of LPS is to produce predictable workflow by creating a coherent set of commitments to coordinate the actions of the participants.

Key components of the milestone planning process are the Big Room for collaborative interaction, wall space for posting of the timeline, a legend for color coding for each stakeholder and sticky notes for posting on the timeline.

The wall timeline will be constrained by several factors: Wall area space available, the number of weeks and overall duration associated with the planning session, the size and number of sticky notes expected to be applied to the timeline.

Information on the sticky notes posted to the milestone plan may include:

- Owner

- Deliverable

- Predecessor (preceding activity and/or constraint)

- Successor (the follow-on activity)

- Risk associated with the activity

- Constraints

Information will vary based on participants and knowledge available at the time of the milestone-planning event. Therefore, it is key to establish the milestone with best-available information (milestone, risk and deliverable at a minimum). The milestone plan should have only enough detail to establish the phases of the project, long-lead items, and any major constraints or handoffs to inform the design deliverables. Work clusters will provide additional detail as they work through their requirements/needs and timing.

Placement of the sticky notes will be adjusted as the team reviews and understands the overall sequencing/workflow of the program. This review process will provide a good framework for the concept "Last Responsible Moment."

Last Responsible Moment: The instant in which the cost of the delay of a decision surpasses the benefit of delay; or the moment when failing to make a decision eliminates an important alternative.

The output will be a macro-level board depiction of the key program sequence, triggers and decision points in the project. This macro-level board will provide content and desired timeframes from which micro-level boards with more granularity can be developed by the project team.

An example of a micro-level board would be the detailed design package strategy, a procurement strategy for material and equipment and timing to support design and construction needs, etc. The micro-level boards eventually will provide timeframes from which the teams can develop mini-level boards or cluster team level plans. All planning should be developed using LPS pull planning approaches.

The milestone plan for a program will be a dynamic document. As the teams develop their respective plans (i.e., design packages, estimating, procurement, logistics, construction), details may develop that affect the initial milestones. The updating/changing of the milestones must be under a change-control process that allows review and agreement by affected parties.

Work Structure and Design Packaging

As the milestone schedule is created and key information handoffs are identified, a design packaging strategy can be developed. Leaders representing all design disciplines and builders must give time and attention to the work-packaging strategy for it to be successful — that is, to ensure that the timelines driven by construction needs are feasible for all inputs to be provided, decisions to be made, and for design to be completed.

You must consult with all project stakeholders to develop alignment and buy-in around what design activity releases what work; and the best medium of communication for providing the information. The packaging strategy must balance the need to discretize and release work early to satisfy the project schedule (i.e., a fast-tracked project may release deep utilities, piles, foundations, and steel) with the tendency to "over-package" or fragment the work. Balance the value of early release with the risk of proceeding on with incomplete information or decisions that are still subject to change.

Once the milestone deliverable has been identified and planned, work clusters initiate a more detailed, discipline-specific plan, pulling back the key design activities, including handoffs between design groups and decisions that need to be made in order to release the work.

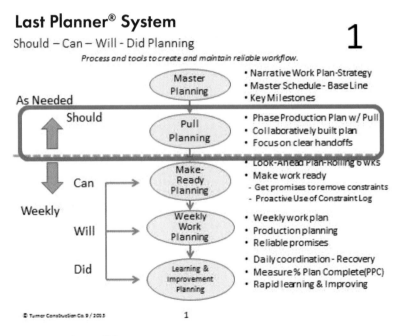

Figure 27: Last Planner® System

Principles for Effective Design Planning

This intentional and thoughtful planning process is crucial for maximizing "positive iteration" for project value, and minimizing rework or "negative iteration" waste.

For effective planning in the design phase, keep these principles in mind:

- Define the work packaging or "chunking" of the project systems and areas (i.e., foundations, first floor steel), to be delivered at the Last Responsible Moment to support the project schedule objectives.

- Create milestones based on the work packaging (i.e., release rebar shop drawings for foundations).

- Plan the project handoffs and decisions, building a network of project-specific commitments.

- Set aside traditional interim review milestones, planning only integration events and final design packages.

- Specificity is key (i.e., I need penetrations in the east wall larger than 4 inches, versus I need final MEP.).

- The purpose of design planning is to have a conversation — strong facilitation is key.

- Use the Big Room "Rules of Engagement" to create a safe and productive working environment.

- Participants must understand and make reliable promises in the planning process. For additional information on Reliable promises refer to "Conversations for Action and Collected Essays: Instilling a Culture of Commitment in Working Relationships, Fernando Flores".

TARGET VALUE DELIVERY (TVD) OVERVIEW Chapter 1

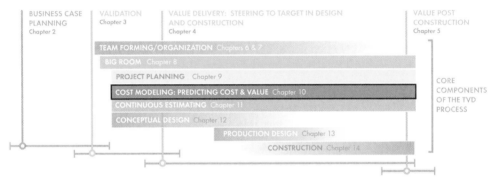

BUSINESS CASE PLANNING Chapter 2	VALIDATION Chapter 3	VALUE DELIVERY: STEERING TO TARGET IN DESIGN AND CONSTRUCTION Chapter 4	VALUE POST CONSTRUCTION Chapter 5

TEAM FORMING/ORGANIZATION Chapters 6 & 7

BIG ROOM Chapter 8

PROJECT PLANNING Chapter 9

COST MODELING: PREDICTING COST & VALUE Chapter 10

CONTINUOUS ESTIMATING Chapter 11

CONCEPTUAL DESIGN Chapter 12

PRODUCTION DESIGN Chapter 13

CONSTRUCTION Chapter 14

CORE COMPONENTS OF THE TVD PROCESS

PHASES OF TVD

Image provided courtesy of Inside Out Consulting and Southland Industries

Scope	August-16	September-16	October-16
Curtainwall	$ 1,487,586	$ 1,509,900	$ 1,524,999
Excavation & Utilities	$ 358,926	$ 344,569	$ 327,341
Foundation	$ 584,962	$ 590,812	$ 584,904
Structural Steel	$ 1,259,635	$ 1,209,250	$ 1,172,972
Concrete	$ 356,284	$ 342,033	$ 342,033
HVAC	$ 2,384,685	$ 2,408,532	$ 2,336,276
Plumbing	$ 984,236	$ 944,867	$ 944,867
Fire Protection	$ 210,000	$ 218,400	$ 227,136
Electrical	$ 1,895,236	$ 1,914,188	$ 1,933,330
Drywall	$ 854,236	$ 811,524	$ 892,677
Misc Trades	$ 4,986,251	$ 5,036,114	$ 5,187,197
Contingency & Escalation	$ 2,304,306	$ 2,299,528	$ 2,321,059
Total Budget	**$ 17,666,343**	**$ 17,629,715**	**$ 17,794,789**
Target Cost	**$ 17,215,500**	**$ 17,215,500**	**$ 17,215,500**

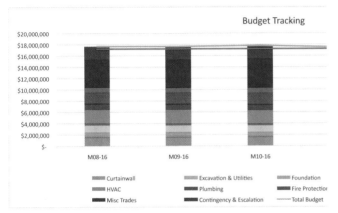

CHAPTER 10

Figure 28: Budget tracking example.

COST MODELING:
PREDICTING COST AND VALUE

- The Cost Modeling Process

- Cost Modeling Requirements

- The IGEDIT Concept

The tools and practices for cost prediction, which have evolved to support traditional Design-Bid-Build project delivery, are primarily focused on producing a cost estimate number based on a given scope of work. In Target Value Delivery (TVD) practice — where scope is evolving through the life of the project — a more sophisticated tracking methodology is required. Scope evolves in TVD as the team explores design sets and works to find a combination of design sets that provide value and meet the owner's CoS.

Spring Valley Hospital - Value Add List					
	COST OF WORK	REJECTED COST	PENDING COST	ACCEPTED COST	NOTES
Women's Center Post Partum & LDR	$ 433,345		$ 433,345		
Public Elevator Lobbies & Bullet Waiting	$ 259,782	$ 259,782			
2nd Floor Public Elevator Lobby	$ 137,772			$133,825	Approved 3.31.16
Letter Sign	$ 35,400			$ 35,400	Approved 3.31.16
Digital Sign	$ 209,109	$ 209,109			3/3/16: Hospital decided not to proceed with
Covered Parking - 12 Spots at Dr's Parking	$ 83,674			$ 83,674	Approved 3.31.16
4th Floor Storage	$ 31,899	$ 31,899			3/3/16: Not proceeding with work
Exterior Painting	$ 254,475	$ 254,475			3/3/16: Operational expense
Nurse Call	$ 106,151			$ 106,151	Approved 3.31.16
Triage	$ 581,815			$ 581,815	Approved 3.31.16
Paint Tower EIFS to Match Existing Pattern					
Total	$ 2,271,193	$ 755,265	$ 433,345	$ 1,078,637	
				$ 900,000	Available Owner Savings Funds
				$ (178,637)	Remaining Funds Available Spring

Figure 29: Cost Model Spreadsheet

The Cost Modeling Process

The cost modeling process begins in the project definition with conceptual estimating. For cost modeling in TVD we need to predict "most likely outcomes" of not just cost but value realization, at any given time in the project, based on current understanding or core project requirements, value decisions already made, and variables for value decisions that still need to be made. Additionally, the project cost model should form a visual system indicating most likely project outcomes, potential variances and impact that remaining decisions could still have.

For most projects currently, this is still as simple as a team spreadsheet or sticky notes on a "TVD" planning section of the Big Room wall with each note representing a risk item, value decision or cost that could add to the total cost of the project.

This starts to create a framework for the objective of the cost model with a few important distinctions. In TVD the initial cost model should be developed before the designer makes the first quantifiable decision. The reason for this is simple: Cost is an input to design rather than an output. Before any design begins, the team should collectively understand the preliminary cost model for the project.

The initial cost model remains an active, continuously updated model for the life of the project. It becomes more informed as the project evolves, and as estimating transforms from benchmarking to conceptual to production.

The ability to reliably predict the cost to complete the work is highly variable across the construction industry. It is not uncommon for companies to find out late in the project that their costs are going to significantly exceed what they estimated, at which point there is no time to react to reduce that cost.

Cost Modeling Requirements

Sound cost modeling requires:

Transparency regarding methodologies: Identify all the companies whose ability to know their cost to complete will impact the overall performance of the project as measured against the Conditions of Satisfaction (CoS).

In a meeting or series of meetings, have each one explain in detail to the team how they project their cost to complete. This often will show how sophistication in this area varies among companies. Companies that are strong at this work should engage with those that are weaker to help raise the overall effectiveness of the cost model.

Risk-and-opportunity tracking: There should be a single list of items that the team perceives either as a risk or an opportunity for the project. Each item has a reference number, a description of what the risk or opportunity is, a likelihood of it happening, the likely cost of it if it did happen, and the net sum of that percentage times that cost. If it also has time, or other CoS-based risk/opportunity, include these in additional fields.

More on Cost Modeling

Ballard, Glenn, "Should Project Budgets Be Based on Worth or Cost?"

Ballard, Glenn and Pennanen, Ari, "Conceptual Estimating and Target Costing"

Ballard, Glenn and Pennanen, Ari, and Haahtela, Yrjana, "Designing to Targets in a Target Costing Process"

An example might be:

- **004:** Material Cost of Copper May Increase; 10%; $47,000: $4,700.

These are added and considered to be part of the projected cost of the project.

Teams need to be encouraged to share incomplete information early. Don't wait until the risk is 80%+ to even tell the rest of the team that it exists.

Set-based design and sound decision making: As the project team evaluates and commits to decisions in TVD, members make decisions in small batches with input from conceptual cost-modeling efforts to select component items against a backdrop of an overall cost model. This is in contrast to traditional delivery, in which estimate updates are prepared in predicted, large-batch cycles (i.e., 30%/60%/90%) and updated at each batch iteration for the entire project.

In TVD the project team needs to track their success at making the best value decisions that fit within the overall project constraints (i.e., cost, time, ROI). This requires a different set of tracking methodologies and tools to support being able to "see the forest while focusing on the trees."

The project team uses risk-and-opportunity tracking to catalog and track the decision-making process against established cost. The purpose here is to make transparent the value-based decision-making process by tracking how various options affect estimated costs and targets across the project.

Ideally, the team provides continuous cost modeling for the options (small-batch estimates) being considered, so value-based decisions are made with full visibility into cost impacts and tested against the validation model and CoS. This requires weighing each decision against the list of value items and analyzing how it will affect the estimate against the target cost.

Effective cost modeling requires the following elements of TVD to be highly formed:

- Team organization

- Functional team organization (See Chapter 6 Forming High Performing teams with Lean Mindsets and Chapter 7 Team Organization and Execution)

- Set-based design and team strategy for basing decision in value

- Project value definition

- Project Conditions of Satisfaction

- Project constraints and target costs

The IGEDIT Concept

Cost modeling supported by set-based design combines value-based decision making (who makes what kind of decisions and when) with evaluation of options developed around each value statement. A good way to think about this process is using the acronym **IGEDIT**, which represents:

- **I**dentify options (Brainstorm Big Ideas)

- **G**ather relevant information: scope, cost, schedule, quality

- **E**valuate options with input across project team based on CoS

- **D**ecide to implement or not using value-based decision-making process

- **I**mplement approved options: release to draw, model, etc.

- **T**est implementation to assumptions

Identify options: The team identifies elements of the project (i.e., types of building skin: curtain wall, EIFS, tilt up precast) and examines against the project definition and targets. These form the design sets of set-based design, which the team wants to reduce to choose the optimal solution.

Key point: The team should strive to minimize the amount of effort to just what is needed to decide on the option. This will minimize rework and wasted effort.

The range of elements that could result in option review includes:

- Big Ideas, i.e., planned options review elements

- Code interpretations or discoveries

- Innovative concepts or applications

- Prefabrication or assembly variations

- Resolution of competing elements of CoS

- Necessary modifications to conflicting elements

- Desired modification to various elements after LRM

- Level of detail development against assumptions

The team might not rely solely on self-identification of options, but also on verifying assumptions in the design and cost model. Key Performance Indicators (KPIs) can be used to test development during the design phase, including design elements that can be readily evaluated against assumptions.

For example, the structural engineer assumed that a structure of this type and size should require an estimated tonnage of steel. As the design progresses, this assumption would be challenged by the evaluation of KPIs (tons/square foot, cost/ton, etc.) against the assumption or target.

Gather relevant information: After developing options and agreeing to a tracking method and format (a value-based decision tool, such as an A3 document), the project team gathers the relevant information required to complete evaluation of the option. While the type of value-based decision tool used often dictates needed information, typical minimum objective needs are: scope definition, affected systems; and variations of option, conceptual cost, and schedule implications.

Subjective information also is necessary to make a final decision around "value." This could include items like aesthetic appeal, complexity of maintenance, employee satisfaction, etc.

Evaluate options: The evaluation and approval of the options should be done in accordance with the team's organizational structure and value-decision process (i.e., by consensus, or leadership team decisions). The key point is that decisions need to be anchored in available data and weighed against the CoS of the project, yet not take the project outside its constraints. Decisions should be deferred to the Last Responsible Moment as driven by the project Milestone Plan.

Depending on the complexity of the evaluation, the team can step through this process using a variety of tools such as Choosing by Advantages, cost/benefit analysis with payback, stakeholder presentations and feedback, etc.

It is helpful for the team to "triage" the option evaluations based on the perceived challenge of arriving at a decision. For example, some option evaluations may be no-brainers, where one option clearly checks all the value boxes and positively affects the project cost and schedule targets; while others will require lengthier evaluation and significant discussion. Apply the rigor where necessary, so valuable time isn't wasted evaluating "no-brainers."

Decide to implement (or not): With the input developed from evaluating options, the team will select the optimal solution with which to proceed to detailed design. If the team cannot arrive at a consensus-based decision from the available data — or an option is too close to call — the team organization should dictate who is the decider for the team (typically the owner's project executive).

Communication and visibility on implementation decisions is critical to make sure the team is coordinated. A value-tracking matrix is updated to reflect the item in the "approved for implementation" stage, and the value-tracking form records the action and date of approval by the team.

Last Responsible Moment Page 162

With an option decision made at the LRM, the team should continually evaluate remaining options to determine if any are affected by this decision (i.e., mutually exclusive options). For example, a decision to go with a curtain wall system would exclude or reduce the options available for a future evaluation of window/glazing types applicable to other skin systems. These dependent options also need to be updated on the tracking matrix, and any excluded items communicated to those team members still working on data gathering and evaluation.

Implement approved options: The option decision releases the designers to further develop the design details (production design) for the project. Since the team strives to expend the minimal amount of effort needed to arrive at a decision and defer much of drawing until the decisions are made, this step releases the designers on production and coordination of the design model to incorporate the chosen option.

During the drawing development, the estimators communicate with the designers on progress of option design and confirmation of initial assumptions as the design is carried forward in detail.

Test implementation: Once the details of the option design are sufficiently developed, the estimating team uses production-estimating methodology to verify the initial objective assumptions and conceptual costs that were used to evaluate the option.

The subjective factors of the option also need to be verified against the original evaluation. If there are any variances in the cost, schedule or value factors of the option in its final state, this needs to be updated on the value-tracking and value-decision forms, so that subsequent decisions are made using the corrected model.

The team also reviews variances as a feedback to the evaluation and decision-making steps to determine any changes that could be made to the process or conceptual cost estimating inputs that will result in more accurate evaluation in the future.

TARGET VALUE DELIVERY (TVD) OVERVIEW   Chapter 1

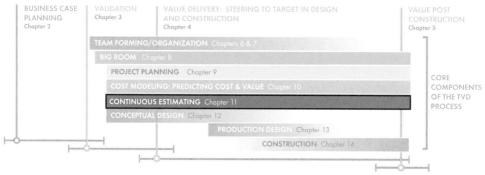

Image provided courtesy of Inside Out Consulting and Southland Industries

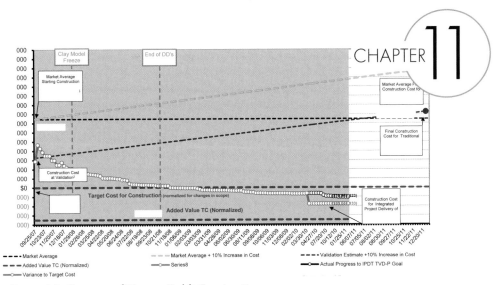

Figure 30: Courtesy of Herrero-Boldt Construction

CONTINUOUS ESTIMATING

- Risk vs. Contingency

- The Estimating Process

- Types of Estimating

For any Target Value Design (TVD) project to succeed, it is critical that the project team has an understanding of the costs associated with value at various levels of detail. Without this, any team would likely struggle making decisions that optimize value within the project constraints.

In broad terms, this is called estimating. Estimating is broken down into several discrete methods and skill sets, potentially supported by different team members at various stages of the project.

In TVD, estimating skills and tools support the team in its cost modeling efforts to predict the most likely project outcome at any given time, based on decisions already made, and remaining decisions and assumptions yet to be clarified. This is a departure in thinking from traditional estimating, which tends to take a single condition (project documents) and predict one outcome, with any variances becoming a change order.

Risk vs. Contingency

It is critical to establish a practice of estimating for ideal conditions and then analyzing for potential obstacles (risks) that could add cost. This requires a high degree of trust among all team members, but especially between builder and owner.

CONTINGENCY DEEP DIVE

As Douglas Lee, Director of Preconstruction with Brasfield and Gorrie, explains, "Contingency, especially hidden contingency, is a barrier to exposing opportunities for improvement because issues are masked. This is the same problem caused by inventory in a production flow. It can also keep a team from making good decisions and feeling 'too comfortable' in having a financial buffer. Really dealing with risk analysis and mitigation forces the team to think about what prevents perfect conditions, and how we can best mitigate to get close to that ideal."

The Estimating Process

- Brainstorm with subject matter experts on what keeps them from being most efficient.

- Focus on what could occur on this project

- Generate the list of potential risks, then gauge probability of occurrence and potential impact. The factoring of probability and potential impact can aid in assigning team priority.

- Assign a champion to lead each effort to investigate options to mitigate and plan out when the decision and/or countermeasure must be implemented to avoid the adverse cost, schedule or quality impact.

- Maintain a focus on risk analysis and mitigation through the life of the project.

Most experienced estimators understand the level of accuracy and typical risk levels at specific design phases, and it is healthy to measure the amount of risk that has specifically been examined against level of accuracy and historic exposure levels. Discuss and come to a team consensus and comfort with risk vs. contingency. This is effective only if all contingency has been isolated and eliminated from within team estimates.

Necessary Skills

How do we know if potential team members have these necessary estimating skills? When selecting and organizing (Chapter 7, Team Organization and Execution), project team members use these or similar questions and considerations for evaluation:

- Please define contingency.

- How do you generate a conceptual estimate?

- How do you determine the right level of detail for a specific estimate?

- Does the format of the reporting function matter?

- What happens when you realize an estimate is inaccurate?

The timing of on-boarding experts in specific areas should support the milestone plan and mapped decision points. These experts may include (but not be limited to) trade partners, design consultants and vendors.

Types of Estimating

1. Cost Benchmarking

- **Definition:** Process of measuring what is feasible by analyzing what has been accomplished in the past and normalizing for present or future conditions, i.e., What can the market yield? Market and condition normalization can be an in-depth process requiring a fair amount of research and understanding of both the current and reference project conditions.

- **When/TVD Phase:** Typically occurs at a high level during Business Case Planning (Chapter 2) and potentially is refined in Validation (Chapter 3). It is often used to validate initial ROI (pro-forma) business case, but must be supported by some level of conceptual estimating (Typically called Rough Order of Magnitude – ROM – budgeting)

- **Overlap with Cost Modeling:** Typically too high a level without sufficient component level detail to engage with Cost Modeling (Chapter 10) at this stage.

- **Level of Accuracy** needed:

  - Best - +/- 10%

  - Good - +/- 15%

  - Note that levels of accuracy for benchmarking vary depending on stage of the project. In Business Case Planning (Chapter 2), often there is insufficient knowledge about the project site or local jurisdictional requirements, so accuracy must be defined within a stated set of assumptions.

  - Benchmark cost development generally is easier for the building itself if the program is sufficiently known. There are project components (i.e., site work) that often have too much variability to accurately estimate this way.

- **Process:**

  - Establish project assumptions

    - Size

    - Scope

    - Aesthetics

    - Project needs

    - Project wants

  - Select reference project(s):

    - Find at minimum one instance of a construction project of similar scope and design level. More reference projects are better.

    - Similar region is better

    - Similar owner is better (to establish design criteria)

- Align similarities and differences in reference projects

- Normalize reference projects for project time, region and scope to reach a benchmark for current project

- Analyze potential risks

- Recommended Practices

  - Manage level of detail; more is better to a point. A basic schedule of values is good, but if scope is unknown, a bottom line value will suffice.

- Considerations

  - What is the economy of the target region?

  - Are there competing projects?

  - Will trade expertise be available locally?

  - Begin the practice of creating transparency into assumptions and potential issues.

- **Risk**

  - Typical

    - Renovations and site work will require a higher level of risk allocation due to the amount of unknown scope.

    - A lot of detail at this level typically is not feasible.

  - Management

    - Begin to consider potential constraints and issues with constructability and local market ramifications.

    - What are their impact to target project costs and schedule?

    - Assign value to these risks. Their total should be in line with the team's comfort level on accuracy.

- **Reporting**

  - Understand the needs of your customers. This should include future estimators, designers, trades and owner; ask them what they need.

- At the benchmarked target cost level, it is critical for the team to understand the assumptions/details of the reference project used to create the benchmark and variances to conditions on this project.

  - This starts to establish cost buckets to be used in conceptual estimating, but the team needs to maintain the flexibility to adjust the tools.

  - Considering the potential for movement of cost and scope between project scope, reporting will be an important factor. There should be negotiation as to level of value for different building aspects, i.e., more importance on energy life cycle costs drives more investment into thermal exterior and mechanical systems versus interior finishes.

- During Business Case Planning (Chapter 2), the owner typically is doing the benchmarking. The handoff should be made quickly to the general construction manager and then to trade partners/builders as soon as possible to begin Validation (Chapter 3) if the initial business case shows feasibility. At validation and through final target cost, the team members, including trades and designers, work to meet the benchmark. As they further refine this metric, the final target cost can be increased as changes to normalizing factors are discovered; or if the owner decides to incorporate proposed items that increase the overall project value at a higher first cost.

2. Conceptual

- **Definition:** Creation of a cost model to estimate likely costs for components supporting program needs, without detailed documentation.

- **When/TVD Phase:** Beginning in Validation (Chapter 3), conceptual estimating starts to predict project-specific costs and is used until sufficient documentation allows for production estimating of components.

- **Overlap with Target Value Tracking:** Conceptual cost modeling provides input to decision making via Cost Modeling (See Chapter 10). Estimators will be required to component items isolated from the overall project cost estimate.

- **Level of Accuracy needed:**

  - Best - +/- 5%

  - Good - +/- 10%

- **Process:**

    - Further develop project assumptions

        - Size

        - Scope

        - Aesthetics

        - Programmatic areas

        - Project needs

        - Project wants

    - Establish project breakdown formatting

        - What is the conditions of satisfaction (CoS) for the team regarding breakdown and formatting?

        - As with reporting, understanding what the need of your customer is important.

        - What will be needed for Cost Modeling (See Chapter 10) to deliver the right information to make decisions?

        - A typical format includes major areas and/or phases with further detail into building components (Uniformat, i.e., building component) or CSI schedule of values.

        - The format needs to be useful to the design team to readily understand assumptions and quantities that make up the concept estimate.

    - Developing the budget

        - Quantities: Establishing quantities allows for measuring for reference and gives guidance to designers and other team members.

        - Ratios from historical data should generate these quantities, i.e., an office building's wall density is typically 5 LF of partition to 1 GSF of floor space.

        - Pricing: Once the quantities for the needed level of detail items have been established, pricing can be applied to represent local market economy.

- Reaching out to subject-matter experts in specific trades in local markets is a good practice.

- Analyze potential risks and opportunities

  - Conceptual is the phase where constructability begins to be vetted and analyzed. Understanding and informing the Milestone Planning (Chapter 9) effort with needed decisions and potential issues and opportunities is essential.

  - As issues and ideas are discovered or uncovered, they should be incorporated into the target value tracking process to be managed and to develop accountability for resolution.

  - This process should also help inform which partners should be on-boarded to the team and on what schedule.

- Recommended Practices

  - Getting to enough detail early is important to aid in establishing and documenting assumptions: informing team planners of needed decisions.

  - Great data makes this effort much simpler; but it can be done by aggregating similar projects to derive average quantity ratios.

- Considerations

  - What is the economy of target region?

  - Are there competing projects?

  - Will trade expertise be available locally?

  - What are governing bodies' constraints on the target region? (i.e., seismic, coastal, flood zone, local AHJs, etc.)

  - What are site-specific phasing constraints?

  - What temporary construction measures will be necessary?

  - What specific safety measures will this project require?

  - Does the format support the effort of Cost Modeling (Chapter 10) and Continuous Estimating?

- **Reporting**
  - Helpful output in addition to cost models will be a high level of anticipated production man-hours to help predict where and when worker peaks may be and aid in analysis of prefabrication ideas and their potential effectiveness.

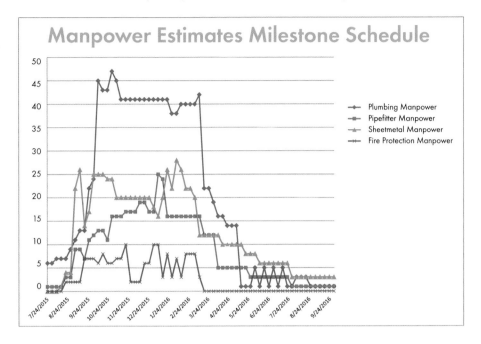

Figure 31: Manpower Loading

- **Who:**
  - Good conceptual estimating is as much art as science and requires strategic outlook; broad understanding of multiple scopes and disciplines; and good operational and constructability knowledge.
  - The general construction estimator typically starts. As trades are engaged in the project, ownership of specific cost buckets are handed off to trade subject matter experts, and the overall cost model becomes a collaborative team effort.

3. Continuous Estimating

- **Definition:** Rather than repeatedly re-estimating the entire project, continuous estimates of small-batch scope items support brainstorming and design set evaluation by providing rough order of magnitude values on the spot. Develop conceptual estimates for components as more detail is provided, and detailed estimates as design solution sets become integrated into the production design. The goal is to arm the team with information needed to make decisions before detailed designs are committed to paper, and then to confirm that information once fully detailed.

- **When/TVD Phase:** Validation, Conceptual (Chapter 12) and Production Design (Chapter 13)

- **Overlap with Cost Modeling:** Cost modeling occurs throughout this effort; small batch budgets inform the project cost model.

- **Level of Accuracy** needed:

  - Best - +/- 5%

  - Good - +/- 10%

- **Process:**

  - Developing the budget

    - The fundamentals of developing overall project cost model are covered in Chapter 10. The difference in this method is that size and scope tend to be smaller; and the timing and estimating should be in-the-moment in support of the team that needs the information.

      - Analyze potential risks and opportunities

        - Risks are similar to other estimating types, but an additional wrinkle is that speed and level of detail will introduce more assumptions.

  - Recommended Practices

    - Create a peer review to avoid gaps, overlaps or mathematical errors because the environment or speed may be different from typical estimate generation.

  - Considerations

- Acknowledge and share that some ideas or design options may be mutually exclusive, and help the team keep this in the forefront as decisions are made. The team must work to define these relationships and create transparency so that energy isn't spent on an idea that already has been excluded by another option chosen.

- It is not standard practice for most estimators to provide estimates and share with a construction team on the fly, without generating a heavy list of caveats and a good measure of contingency — encouragement of this desired behavior requires a trusted team environment and consistently revisiting initial assumptions to update cost expectations.

- **Who:**

  - Estimators will need a high level of confidence and ability to work collaboratively in a team. They should be able to accept critique by team members and generate a level of trust with other estimators. Prior experience with conceptual estimating and a knowledge of "what things should cost" is critical so as not to rely on computer-aided estimating tools that generally require a high level of detail for accurate estimates.

4. Production Estimating

- **Definition:** This is the most traditional form of estimating. It is driven heavily by pricing and planning that has been documented in design. It verifies assumptions and that what was designed can be built based on what we developed during earlier conceptual stages.

- **When/TVD Phase:** Value Delivery (Chapter 4), and Production Design (Chapter 13).

- **Overlap with Cost Modeling:** Production estimating confirms the predictions made via cost modeling.

- **Level of Accuracy** needed:

  - Best - +/- 1%

  - Good - +/- 3%

- **Process:**

  - Developing the budget

- Confirm the breakdown and pricing isolations needed by the team: areas, phases, issue or decision-laden areas.

- Analyze the construction phase plan to understand when and how building components will come together.

- Survey the design for quantities of building materials, and then apply pricing to those materials as well as installation productivities (labor) and the equipment necessary to facilitate this construction.

- Temporary construction measures should also be addressed.

- Safety plans should be established, vetted and priced.

- Form a running list of assumptions for scopes or items not documented in design, plus potential issues and unclear scope.

- Analyze potential risks and opportunities

  - There is a common industry risk of pricing only what is documented, and not offering constructability comments on concerns and ideas based on additional details that builders might need to provide clarity.

- Recommended Practices

  - Remember the value of this effort is truly providing for the team:

    - High level of accuracy

    - Detailed analysis of constructability

    - Efficient and effective means of documenting and sharing contractibility risks and assumptions, plus opportunities for improvement

    - Confirmation of the team's conceptual ideas

    - Discussing production goals that are forming the basis of the estimate

- Considerations

  - Remember the customer of this product is more than just the designers, team members and owner; the construction team will need to use this product to aid in building, tracking and forecasting throughout the project.

- The detailed production estimate format needs to be developed with the above customers to support actual cost and productivity tracking, as well as provide feedback to any future benchmarking data.

5. Forecasting Estimating/Cost Tracking

- **Definition:** Estimating is the art of predicting the costs of a project by utilizing prior project experience and knowledge as a tool. Once we start to spend actual costs on the project, whether in design or construction, forecasting becomes the art of collecting data on spend vs. progress to date, and adjusting the expectations set from the estimate for actual project conditions.

- **When/TVD Phase:** Value Delivery

- **Overlap with Target Value Tracking:** Target Value Tracking

- **Level of Accuracy** needed:

  - Best - +/- 1%

  - Good - +/- 3%

- **Process:**

  - Cost forecasting takes various forms depending on the type of cost, i.e.: general condition, subcontracts, materials, labor, etc.

  - The team's general conditions are typically evaluated on a per-unit basis (i.e., trailer cost per month) against the estimate during the mobilization of the project, and once a consistent burn rate is established, the update is most significantly impacted by changes in the duration of the project. Aggregating general-conditions items within the team can be helpful in reducing costs.

  - For subcontracts, the estimate is carried until a commitment is made to a subcontractor. If this is in the form of a GPM or Lump Sum, the only remaining forecast is to gauge the level of change orders anticipated and project an appropriate additional cost.

  - Commitments need to be tracked in terms of quantity required and unit cost. As initial purchases are made, or project-wide pricing is negotiated, the forecast is updated periodically based on remaining materials still needing to be purchased to complete the project, and actual purchase prices achieved vs. the estimate.

- The most significant variable of cost is labor productivity and crew cost.

  - Productivity measurement follows the framework and project areas established in the estimating phase of the work.

  - As work is put in place, compare the effort expended (typically man hours) for a completed quantity of work against the production rate assumed in the estimate.

  - This needs to be completed on a per-work-type and per-area on a weekly cycle.

  - With each incremental measurement in actual productivity, the projection for remaining costs is updated.

  - The intention of implementing Lean strategies that reduce waste and improve flow is to positively affect productivity over the life of the project.

  - Actual production rates achieved should feed back to the estimating groups to refine the starting point of cost expectations on future projects.

- **Who:**

  - Cost forecasting and productivity measurement is typically executed at the Value Realization stage of the project with the data input from project management and Last Planner® personnel.

While the various tools for cost modeling throughout the life of the project are skill sets required within the project team, an additional skill that needs to be developed by the owner is establishing allowable and target costs for overall objectives of the project. These methods are anchored in needs established in the business plan and prior project history (when available) within the owner's portfolio.

Setting Allowable and Target Costs

- **Definition:** Allowable costs are defined during Business Case Planning (Chapter 2) and set out the most the owner is willing/able to spend on the project in absolute terms (or to anchor to project objectives). A target cost is a tool to create tension within a team to drive innovation to improve cost outcomes.

- **When/TVD Phase:** The allowable costs are set during Business Case Planning (Chapter 2) phase and should be revisited if the Validation (Chapter 3) changes. Target costs are set through team alignment as sufficient confidence is established in the cost and design definition.

- **Overlap with Cost Modeling:** Allowable cost targets establish the baseline for measuring value benefit against cost. Value tracking can affect allowable cost if a value benefit is determined to improve the business case.

- **Level of Accuracy** needed:

  - Allowable costs - variable depending on business risk tolerance of owner.

  - Target cost - +/- 4%

- **How to establish a target cost**

  - Effective target costs require team alignment and buy-in, yet maintain a healthy tension that encourages the team to be more innovative than normal in order to reach the goal. There is a role of "visionary leader" (often the owner) to assure the target is challenging enough, yet expressed in methodology that can be understood by any team member.

  - **Method 1:** If a reference project from the owner (or very similar market history) is available:

    - Use output from the benchmarking process initiated earlier.

    - Perform detailed team research into reference project scope and costs.

    - Go into a deep-dive normalizing the project for current location cost difference.

    - Normalizing factors include jurisdictional requirements imposed by AHJ, final programmatic differences, geographical cost difference, and inflation. Typically estimated site costs are too variable to normalize on their own.

    - Normal design trade-off decision that teams make as part of every project are not considered normalizing factors. For example, if the reference project chose to install a lower-quality flooring product to be able to "buy" another scope item, this is not a normalizing factor.

- A simple, summary format supports clearly delineating the reference projects, geographic/market cost adjustment, inflation, and normalizing factors.

- **Method 2:** If no reference project is available (i.e., unique renovations or first-time builds):

  - Take a deeper dive into finding reference projects that share similarities at a component level (i.e., structural system, skin, etc.)

  - Follow the benchmarking methodology for each component that can be isolated and related to the current project conditions.

  - For any building components that cannot be isolated or have no reference benchmark, use conceptual estimating to complete the picture of the whole program.

  - There may be more negotiation required on the conceptual components within the team to achieve the right conceptual estimate value to serve as a target.

  - Once consensus is achieved around all component level benchmarked target costs – and conceptually estimated cost – assemble the components into an overall target.

- **Reporting**

  - The target cost must be clearly documented including the method by which the target was established from reference project or components. Showing the work in this case is critical for consensus understanding and consistent buy in.

  - Once the target is set, this also needs to be reported on the cost-forecasting and value-tracking tools the team is using to provide a clear indication of progress toward the goal.

- **Who**

  - Allowable cost establishment requires financial and executive input at the owner level to determine what is feasible within the business case. Setting successful target costs requires owner and team participation, including key financial stakeholders and estimators, as well as a commitment to data collection on the owner's portfolio on prior project history and normalization factors.

TARGET VALUE DELIVERY (TVD) OVERVIEW   Chapter 1

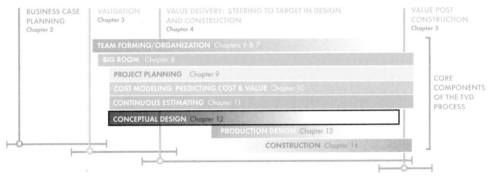

BUSINESS CASE PLANNING
Chapter 2

VALIDATION
Chapter 3

VALUE DELIVERY: STEERING TO TARGET IN DESIGN AND CONSTRUCTION
Chapter 4

VALUE POST CONSTRUCTION
Chapter 5

TEAM FORMING/ORGANIZATION   Chapters 6 & 7

BIG ROOM   Chapter 8

PROJECT PLANNING   Chapter 9

COST MODELING: PREDICTING COST & VALUE   Chapter 10

CONTINUOUS ESTIMATING   Chapter 11

CONCEPTUAL DESIGN   Chapter 12

PRODUCTION DESIGN   Chapter 13

CONSTRUCTION   Chapter 14

CORE COMPONENTS OF THE TVD PROCESS

PHASES OF TVD

Image provided courtesy of Inside Out Consulting and Southland Industries

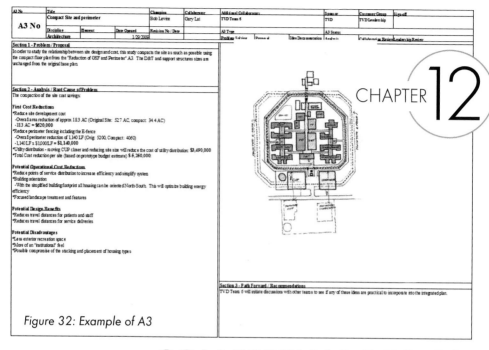

CHAPTER 12

A3 No	Title			Champion	Collaborator	Additional Collaborators		Sponsor	Customer Group	Sign-off
A3 No	Compact Site and perimeter			Bob Levine	Gary Lai	TVD Team 6		TVD	TVD Leadership	
	Discipline	Element	Date Opened	Revision No / Date		A3 Type		A3 Status		
	Architecture		1/29/2009			Problem Solving	Proposal	Idea Documentation	Analysis	Collaboration Review/Leadership Review

Section 1 - Problem / Proposal

In order to study the relationship between site design and cost, this study compacts the site as much as possible using the compact floor plan from the "Reduction of GSF and Perimeter" A3. The D&T and support structures sizes are unchanged from the original base plan.

Section 2 - Analysis / Root Cause of Problem

The compaction of the site cost savings:

First Cost Reductions
*Reduce site development cost
    -Overall area reduction of approx 18.3 AC (Original Site: 52.7 AC, compact: 34.4 AC)
    -18.3 AC = $620,000
*Reduce perimeter fencing including the E-fence
    -Overall perimeter reduction of 1,140 LF (Orig: 5200, Compact: 4060)
    -1,140 LF x $1,000 LF = $1,140,000
*Utility distribution - moving CUP closer and reducing site size will reduce the cost of utility distribution: $3,490,000
*Total Cost reduction per site (based on prototype budget estimate) $ 5,250,000:

Potential Operational Cost Reductions
*Reduce points of service distribution to increase efficiency and simplify system
*Building orientation
    -With the simplified building footprint all housing can be oriented North-South. This will optimize building energy efficiency
*Focused landscape treatment and features

Potential Design Benefits
*Reduces travel distances for patients and staff
*Reduces travel distances for service deliveries

Potential Disadvantages
*Less exterior recreation space
*More of an "institutional" feel
*Possible compromise of the stacking and placement of housing types

Section 3 - Path Forward / Recommendations

TVD Team 6 will initiate discussions with other teams to see if any of these ideas are practical to incorporate into the integrated plan.

Figure 32: Example of A3

CONCEPTUAL DESIGN

- The 4 Phases of Conceptual Design

- Work Cluster Research Tools

- Vetting Ideas

Conceptual design kicks-off value delivery and steering to the target. As the project transitions from validation to design delivery, the team gathers to develop and generate opportunities and ideas using the tools and approaches described in this chapter.

Four key aspects of this phase, which the team delivers in ongoing cycles are:

1. **Criteria Development**

2. **Organizing Information**

3. **Set-based Design and Evaluation**

4. **Integration**

The cycle from abstract to specific drives innovation — from ideas through concepts to a well-developed specific design. This is the goal of the conceptual phase.

1. Criteria

The work of developing and aligning around Conditions of Satisfaction (CoS) and other criteria should be done prior to the transition into conceptual design. It is imperative that the team move into this phase with clear understanding of the project CoS, criteria and needs. Moving forward with any lack of clarity or alignment puts the team at high risk for rework and creating waste in the process.

2. Organizing Information

In the conceptual phase, we organize the overall design strategy into chunks to meet the needs of permitting, construction, long-lead equipment or material, pre-purchase packages, etc. This knowledge also will provide an idea of what resources and specialty design skills/services are required (i.e., vibration, soils engineering) and which areas require ideation and exploration.

The project team identifies Last Responsible Moments for decision or converging points for the design as intermediate milestones. Then the team determines the appropriate work cluster(s) to take on the development of the research and evaluation needed to lead to a sound decision.

Last Responsible Moment, Page 162

3. Set-based Design and Evaluation

Set-based design is based on the idea that as teams break the work into chunks or components, multiple options should be explored at a level that will allow the team to make a sound and informed decision, at the right time. Sets or alternates or Big Ideas should be narrowed by considering the solutions in the context of the whole: the CoS, other criteria, cost model, schedule impact and value.

Typically designers want to make decisions and narrow options on projects as quickly as possible in order to be able to move forward — quite often stating that they don't have time in the schedule to wait. The flip side to that is when unsound decisions are made or decisions are forced too soon without understanding the impact on the whole, then a wrong decision needs to be undone, revisited, or worse, the opportunity to consider other options is lost. By slowing down decision-making appropriately, exploring reasonable options, and making decisions anchored in objective factors, teams actually deliver projects faster. This time improvement happens because we reduce re-work — often called value engineering in this phase.

Sets may be developed by the project team in an integration event and by the work clusters. Regardless, the decision point and path to reach a sound decision must be integrated with the team's milestone plan.

Work Clusters, Page 61

Sets are then released to work clusters to investigate relevant information as required to support a decision about each set or Big Idea under consideration. Site visits and subject matter experts play key roles in this work. The teams report their findings that were tested against the CoS and criteria in simple set-tracking logs.

Design Work Cluster Research Tools

Benchmarks and Best Practices

An initial step for a work cluster is to more deeply research the past work that the current project has been benchmarked against during validation (Chapter 3). Work clusters may seek reliable solutions that currently exist and owner practices that can be re-used by the project team as already-vetted solutions. This design tool is based on external research of similar completed projects with similar business cases.

Analogous Projects

This is a key opportunity to think expansively. If customer experience is a value in an airport security project, where has that been most effectively solved? What can we learn from analogous industries such as retail or hospitality? Additional research can be performed in order to extract applicable design elements that can influence the current project.

Retrospectives of Current State

This design tool is applicable when a team is being asked to develop a project type that the customer is currently using (i.e., renovation, expansion or relocation). A retrospective of the current state can provide the design team with elements that the new project needs to address. These could fall in the realm of adoption or alteration of things that work and omission or alteration of things that don't work.

This opportunity is to dive deep into what works/doesn't work, to determine the "why" and ensure the team is solving the right problem. Current state exploration allows us to change the design practice of simply fixing what is wrong to really designing the right solution for the value proposition.

Intuition

This is not necessarily a "tool," but rather is based on skill sets that designers often possess. As a profession, designers excel in extracting values or CoS from the customer and converting this information into a built environment. Traditionally, end-users prescriptively instruct designers on what they want or don't want. The design team should use this information to answer "why" they want or don't want something. This can result in opportunities for innovation.

End-User Journey

This design tool is mapping out how the end-user will move or use the space within the project. This is most effective when the team physically walks through a similar space with the end-users. A simple set of questions guide the journey:

- What are the different steps in the journey?

- What are the operational and experiential needs of each step?

- How might people, process, space or technology be used to address these needs?

Process Mapping

Lean value stream maps are an effective tool focused on value, waste and countermeasures for a particular process. They connect directly to the end-user's value proposition: If the goal is shorter stays in a hospital setting or decreased walking distance in a hotel, what can each process step contribute to this end? When used effectively, process mapping can help the team reduce design time. The team designs the experience and operations before it designs the space. The architecture is the enabler of the experience and operations.

Vetting Ideas

The work clusters share the ideas with each other in a series of integration events and present organized and filtered sets to the group.

Integration Event, Page 73

Ideas with the biggest potential to affect the project's success factors are categorized as Big Ideas; while easy-to-achieve ideas with high impact are considered no-brainers. As the process continues, the work clusters add more ideas and develop selected ones to better understand the impacts to the key project metrics.

At the conclusion of each Integration Event the impacts of the options are reviewed to determine progress toward goals. The work clusters prepare the information in an A3 format to take back to the project team in an integration event. A well-executed A3 will represent alignment of all stakeholder perspective and will present a recommendation to the team.

A3, Page 159

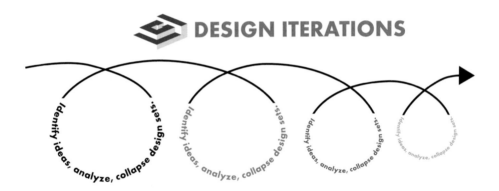

Figure 33: Design Iterations

The work during conceptual design is to pare down the design sets with rational analysis to establish a more defined scope of the project. The work clusters research and develop each "set" to a minimum level of detail needed to drive to a decision. Decisions are based on whether there is sufficient value added to substantiate the cost schedule and impact along with the alignment to the CoS and other project criteria.

Once work clusters eliminate design sets based on "least amount of work necessary to remove options," additional detail is developed for remaining possible solution sets. The overriding objective is that work clusters continue to add level of detail as solution sets are eliminated to pare down possible solutions to be the optimal one.

The project team continues this cycle of work it collectively decides it is ready to transition agreed-upon concepts to production or more detailed work. The agreed-upon concepts are combined into a single design. It remains critical that the team continues to test the options as they become integrated and more detailed against the project criteria and cost model.

Conceptual design transitions to production design at the point at which a singular design concept emerges that captures the selected design sets and is embraced by all stakeholders (owners, users, designers, builders, etc.). The emerging design might still have some unresolved sets to be explored. Enough of the sets should have been narrowed to release the majority of the work to production design. To move forward, the team should be aligned that the design can be constructed within, at, or below allowable cost and meet the CoS and other criteria.

TARGET VALUE DELIVERY (TVD) OVERVIEW   Chapter 1

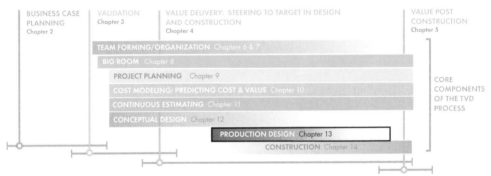

Image provided courtesy of Inside Out Consulting and Southland Industries

CHAPTER 13

Figure 34: BIM model graphic used courtesy of UHS and Southland

PRODUCTION DESIGN

- When Production Design Begins

- Framework for Production Design

- Work Clusters/Offline Work

The transition to production design occurs at the moment in which final design concepts are accepted by the project team, including owners and users, and have been validated as aligning with the CoS and cost model. The design sets represent the best combination of options determined by the team to optimize owner value. In addition, the team now has a high confidence that the design can be achieved at or below allowable cost.

Framework for Production Design

Similar to conceptual design, the framework for production design typically takes the form of offline work clusters and regularly scheduled Integration Events in the Big Room. It typically kicks off with a level-setting meeting in the Big Room (Chapter 8).

Integration Event, Page 73

Topics covered at that meeting and subsequent events include:

- Production design pull plan
  - Organize sets/activities based on construction needs
    - Permitting
    - BIM coordination
    - Package release for construction
  - Reassess the speed of the work and the frequency of the Big Room events in a pull plan session
  - Review of cost model
  - Work cluster report outs
  - Lean learning
  - Hot topics

The pull plan serves as the road map for work happening within work clusters as driven by the milestone plan. Each project needs to assess the level of detail required for a pull plan.

Milestone Plan, Page 87

At this point the teams should pay attention to which entity is producing the work. If a specialty trade is on board, should the detailing and/or modeling pass to them, and at what point? The builders and designers must stay closely linked to remain on track with the cost model as the detail develops.

The figures are a detail of the pull plan; variance codes for use when tasks are not completed as promised; a Planned Percent Complete log illustrating the holiday season impact on the team performance, and an example pull plan sticky.

Work Clusters/Offline Work

Offline work by work clusters or individuals balances the work in the Big Room. The detailed pull plan guides the offline work. Each task is responsive to the needs of another, and optimally is addressed in the specified order. Specific details of the project (i.e., ceiling plans, casework, elevations, finishes and fixtures) are created and reviewed with users and the project team. Project values, including cost, continue to guide this work. Progress against the cost model is prepared and posted.

Ideation continues in this phase of design. Prefab opportunities continue to emerge; those developed during concept design are developed to be implementable. For equipment-intensive projects, this is a time of focused coordination: space, infrastructure and budget.

BIM coordination is sequenced according to the needs of the project and should be identified in the pull plan with clear output objectives. Coordination events should be held often to align the work being done in small batches.

Production design often transitions to construction through release of packages per the milestone plan. More and more projects are being built using package-release approaches. The team often is in both phases at the same time.

Big Room events should be scheduled to support the activities of both phases and to keep the team highly coordinated and focused on the project targets, criteria and CoS.

TARGET VALUE DELIVERY (TVD) OVERVIEW   Chapter 1

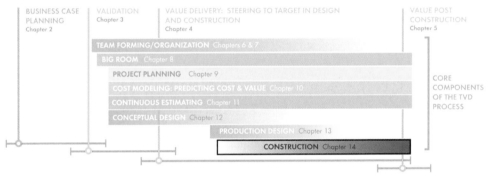

Image provided courtesy of Inside Out Consulting and Southland Industries

CHAPTER 14

CONSTRUCTION

- 7 Practices and Lean Construction Elements

As production design starts to release work to the field for coordination, pre-fabrication and construction, the focus of the Target Value Delivery (TVD) process transitions to supporting the last planners in execution of the work and measuring actual execution against targets. In the construction phase TVD is supported by the following practices and lean construction elements:

1. **Prefabrication**

2. **Team tracking of labor productivity**

3. **Last Planner® System**

4. **Eliminating waste in the construction process**

5. **Reimagining the role of the designer during construction**

6. **Blurring the line between contracts**

7. **Change management**

Figure 35: Last Planners in the Field

It is beyond the scope of this book to provide an in-depth how-to into each of these elements since they are detailed out in other currently available publications. However, we will briefly review each here in overview and to discuss need and impact to the overall target value delivery process.

1. Prefabrication

Prefabrication planning needs to begin during design so that components and assemblies can be explored by the design team and the design coordinated with these as needed. It continues during coordination when these prefabrication elements (i.e., corridor racks, bathroom pods or in-wall utilities) are coordinated within the virtual model of the project (BIM or traditional coordination drawings).

Significant benefits can be derived from multi-trade prefabrication of building elements that move work into a manufacturing setting (off-site or near site) where work can happen in a controlled, safe environment that facilitates high-quality workmanship. To help facilitate multi-trade assemblies, often the general contractor will lead the effort to establish an off-site warehouse where multiple trades can work on these assemblies together.

Prefabrication planning should be mapped out as part of Project Planning (Chapter 9). Often, prefabrication assembly will need to begin well before normal stick built activities take place. This will also allow the team to capture the maximum schedule benefits from pre-fabrication, as building components can be created while site, foundation or structural work is still in progress.

2. Team Tracking of Labor Productivity

Cost, labor manpower and labor productivity tracking are explained in Continuous Estimating, Chapter 11. In a TVD model, this becomes a team activity in that labor productivities must not be measured in silos. For example, the last planners may make a conscious decision to allow the plumbing installation to occur before the drywall framing. This will show on productivity trackers as a significant beating of targets for the plumbing trades, and likely a shortfall for framing. The key is, does one more than offset the other? If productivity trade-offs yield a net project savings, then the team as a whole is benefitting from the decision.

It is generally accepted that once the design is substantially complete and most materials and traditional subcontracts are procured, labor productivity is one of the most significant variable costs remaining on the project. Since design and scope decisions are made during the initial phases of a project based on expected cost outcomes, results from actual productivity measurement should be re-incorporated into the project cost forecasting.

From a TVD perspective, this will show the team if there are any anticipated cost savings, and if so the team can weigh the confidence of those savings to be realized, which could be re-invested in value-add items that were not achievable based on earlier cost predictions of the project.

3. Last Planner® System

As one of the core tools of Lean Construction practice, the Last Planner® System (LPS) provides a framework for engaging the people most directly managing value creation in the field (i.e. superintendents and foremen) to collaboratively establish the installation flow and sequence for optimal throughput of work on the site. Additionally, LPS has a built in PDCA cycle that allows the team to improve the planning process on an ongoing basis.

PDCA, Page 163

Implementing LPS as the planning process supports TVD in establishing the connected conversations necessary to find productivity improvement opportunities and eliminating waste in the field. Additionally, a focus of LPS planning methods is looking ahead for constraints, which assists the preconstruction and design team members in supporting the last planners in meeting their objectives.

4. Eliminating Waste in the Construction Process

Another core tenet of Lean Construction is a focus on the elimination of waste in every step of the process. Throughout validation and conceptual design, the project team is making scope decisions based on a confidence level in the cost feedback the team is providing towards that scope. Through Lean Construction practices, actual costs should be less than — and productivities higher than — traditional construction delivery methods. Waste elimination and the impact thereof on the project cost, needs to be a part of the ongoing conversation during design and estimating; the team must make assumptions initially on the impact of these measures on total project costs, and through productivity tracking determine the validity of the assumptions as the project progresses.

5. Reimagining the role of the designer during construction

In a traditional delivery method, as the project transitions from design to construction, and contractors are engaged to execute the work described in the project documents, the designer's role transitions to management, oversight and protection of owner (and self) interests. In a collaborative TVD process, it's understood that the design is not truly complete once construction begins; as well, designers are not creating implementation documents for unknown entities — builders are generally sitting at the table while design documents are being prepared.

In this type of collaborative environment, the designer's role during the construction process becomes more of facilitation, problem solving and supportive engagement to assist the build team in executing the project, even at times reconsidering the original design intent and implementation drawings. When conflicts, errors or installation mistakes are discovered, the designer now is engaged in helping the team discover the most cost-effective method for accomplishing the intent of the design, even if the documents are not matched exactly.

Additionally, the designer takes an active role in seeking constructability feedback and input from the builders, facilitating retrospective events on the effectiveness of the design documents and installation details, so that future documents can be improved with that feedback.

6. Blurring the line between contracts

Traditional construction proposals and contracts typically overflow with inclusions, exclusions, and attempts to shift risk on to another party. Contracts in a TVD project are different, and focus the group on managing risk collectively and putting those most capable of mitigating a risk in a position to actually do so.

To do this, the lines between contracts need to be blurred to make it simple to transfer scope from one contract to another that is better able to manage that risk.

A good example of this on a project is the issue of supplemental steel.

Blurring the Lines on a Steel Contract

On a typical steel building the steel contractor installs all of the structural steel on the project, but there are typically several other contractors that need steel to support elements of their work, such as mechanical, plumbing, electrical, owner-furnished equipment, etc.

The trade contractor on a typical project may have a contract clause that requires it to install all steel associated with their contract in an effort to avoid scope gaps. However, they are typically not efficient at installing steel, and for that reason the cost for these contractors to install steel is far higher than the cost per unit to have the steel contractor install that same steel.

In TVD, the team should be collaborating early in design to determine what additional steel is required for other trades. That steel can then be incorporated into the steel contractor's scope of work at a lower cost than putting it into the individual contracts of the contractors utilizing the steel.

It is important that contract terms support TVD by breaking down barriers between parties. As is often referenced in the Lean Construction community, "buildings leak at the intersection of contracts," and contracts supporting TVD seek to minimize those intersections to facilitate a higher level of collaboration and performance.

7. Change-management system

The change-management system on a TVD project should feel very different from a traditional change-management system. A TVD change-management system has the following characteristics:

1. It is the single clearinghouse for owner-requested program changes.

2. Only changes that get reviewed and approved through this system can be implemented.

3. It reviews the impact on the entire CoS (for many changes, few if any of the CoS will be affected, so this need not be a burdensome system).

4. Ideally it is a system that reviews these items with an integrated team of designers, builders and owners. On complex projects it is impossible for any one person or discipline to know that a change is "small" or "minor."

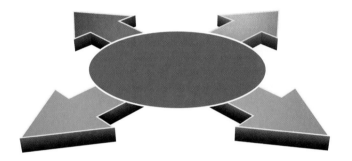

THE PATH FORWARD

Target Value Delivery (TVD) is a constantly evolving process. This book strives to outline and explain the current best practices within the industry. Fortunately, there is an innovative and enthusiastic body of practitioners who are constantly striving to improve the way that buildings are delivered by improving the processes used to deliver them.

We hope the information in this manual will serve as a foundation from which you and your team can build a strong TVD process for your project. Inherent in the Lean culture is the desire to continually learn and build upon experience. We strongly encourage incorporating the best practices from this manual into your project delivery system and then striving to improve processes through lessons learned and retrospective.

CONTRIBUTORS

EXECUTIVE EDITORS

KRISTIN Hill

Kristin Hill is President/Lean Consultant at InsideOut Consulting Inc.

"Collaboration changes everything. My entire 35-year career has been focused on continuously improving the delivery of design and construction services. My passion has been collaboration for the purpose of producing increased value for my clients and delivering projects that meet their highest goals."

Kristin brings 10 years of Lean consulting expertise to the design and construction industry. Prior to her career as a Lean consultant, Kristin founded, grew and subsequently sold an architectural firm in the Boston Area. Her firm was recognized by Architectural Record as the Best Managed Small Firm, in part for its collaborative philosophy.

Currently Kristin provides coaching to teams for projects being delivered using Lean principles and tools. She has coached project teams implementing Lean on a wide range of project sizes, from $500,000 to $6 billion; and a wide range project types, including a commercial border crossing facility, Naval barracks, medical and behavioral health hospitals, airports and theme park attractions.

Kristin is an approved Last Planner® System coach. She is Chair of Lean Construction Institute (LCI) Standards Committee and is a contributing author to the LCI manual Transforming Design and Construction, a Framework for Change. Kristin regularly speaks at LCI and other industry events.

KATHERINE **Copeland**

Katherine Copeland, P.E., is a Project Executive with Southland Industries, one of the largest MEP building systems firms in the nation. She has spent the last 22 years with Southland involved with the design and construction of mechanical systems for facilities located across the county from Washington, D.C., to California and even Hawaii. Her early career focused on hospitality industry projects; however, in recent years that focus has shifted to the healthcare industry.

For the past 10 years she has focused on the design and construction of healthcare facilities, both new construction and renovation of existing operational facilities. She is focused on delivering value to the end-user through collaboration and operational excellence in project delivery. In 1998, when Lean Construction Institute (LCI) formed, Katherine was fortunate to be involved with early training and implementation of Last Planner® System on several Southland projects and had the opportunity to see first-hand the quality and efficiency improvements associated with Lean.

Since then she has continued to develop her Lean knowledge. Katherine has worked on expanding Lean and Integrated Project Delivery (IPD) throughout the lifecycle of projects as well as developing a Lean culture with her teams.

She is on the Core Group of the Carolina Communities of Practice and is part of the LCI Education Committee. She received her bachelor's degree in architectural engineering from Pennsylvania State University.

CHRISTIAN **Pikel**

Christian Pikel supports Universal Health Systems (UHS) as Regional Project Manager leading Integrated Project Delivery (IPD) teams in improving project outcomes via rapid team development; high levels of integration; and development of innovations to UHS systems and practices. He also leads innovation efforts to improve operations within the UHS Design and Construction Dept.

Christian has spent the last 18 years in the design and construction industry, with the last eight years focused on healthcare.

DICK Bayer

Dick Bayer is the former Executive Director of Lean Construction Institute (LCI) and current President of The ReAlignment Group. He has been deeply engaged in construction-project collaboration and alignment partnering since 2003; and part of the Lean community since 2008. He was one of the chief facilitators for the largest Integrated Project Delivery (IPD) project ever – the $7 billion California Health Care Receivership Program.

Since 2010 his firm has participated in more than 100 Lean or IPD programs with 200+ teams across the country and abroad. He has been the lead instructor of LCI Target Value Delivery (TVD) workshops throughout the country.

BERNITA Beikmann

Bernita Beikmann, AIA, EDAC, LSSBB, is a Principal with HKS Inc. (Dallas office) and Director of Lean Strategy for the office. She graduated from Kansas State University with a bachelor's of Architecture and Certificate in Regional and Community Planning in 1996. She is a registered architect in Texas, California, Florida, Washington, Ohio, Indiana, Washington, D.C., and Nevada.

Bernita has been with HKS for 19 years and has spent the last 17 years primarily on healthcare projects. The last nine years she has focused on Integrated Project Delivery (IPD) and Lean project improvement on projects and with project teams. She is a successful advocate for Lean planning, design and construction.

Bernita has served in integral roles as a project architect and project manager and as a coach and facilitator for project teams. As Director of Lean Strategy and a Lean Six Sigma Black Belt, she works with all departments at HKS to improve internal processes. She has shared her expertise with more than 12 organizations and conferences and was one of the original Core Team members of the Dallas-Fort Worth Lean Construction Institute (LCI) Community of Practice. She currently serves on the joint committee for The American Institute of Architects and Associated General Contractors of America.

STANLEY **Chiu**

Stan Chiu, AIA, LEED AP, is a Principal with HGA Architects and Engineers. He is a collaborative leader, an architect motivated to assemble and direct high performance teams and practices to serve fundamental human needs. He is an industry leader in the application of Lean Integrated Project Delivery (IPD) principles and tools to project design and delivery. He has helped develop many core Lean IPD tools such as Target Value Delivery and Set-Based Design through work with clients such as Samsung, Sutter Health, the California Prison Receivership (CPR) and Universal Health Services (UHS).

He promotes an integrated team approach, enlisting the knowledge and expertise of planners, designers, contractors, owners and consultants early in the design process to deliver an efficient, cost-effective facility.

Stan's projects have received national and local The American Institute of Architects (AIA) awards. He has published extensively and lectured on Lean IPD at venues such as national and local AIA conferences, national and local Lean Construction Institute (LCI) conferences, University of California (Berkeley) , Cal Poly San Luis Obispo, Walt Disney Imagineering, Samsung Corp., Hoag Health System and Arcadis International.

DIGBY **Christian**

Digby Christian is the Director of Integrated Lean Project Delivery for Sutter Health, a not-for-profit healthcare provider in Northern California. He leads Sutter's effort to create a work environment that supports understanding what's valuable to the client and encourages teams to actively and continually figure out how to align their work practices with delivering that value.

This has required changing the way project teams look at risk, contracts, estimating, work planning, design and construction coordination, supply chain management and production tracking. This has led to a radically different project team culture of engaged, continuous reflection and improvement, and of mutual respect and accountability.

Previously, as a project manager, he lead the effort to establish best-in-class Integrated Project Delivery (IPD) processes on Sutter's $2.5 billion investment in new acute care facilities in San Francisco Bay Area.

Digby is an active participant in Lean Construction Institute (LCI) Knowledge Transfer Sessions, which seek to spread what is being learned by leading Lean practitioners. He also is a supporter of and an engaged contributor to the effort of University of California, Berkeley, Project Production Systems Laboratory (P2SL). He is a contributing author to the LCI manual Transforming Design and Construction, a Framework for Change.

CHRIS **Dierks**

Chris Dierks is the East Coast Leader of Lean Construction and Integrated Project Delivery (IPD) for DPR Construction. He earned a bachelor's of science degree in Construction Science and Management from Kansas State University in 1998. He has worked in a variety of leadership roles in the construction industry for more than 18 years on a wide range of technically challenging projects.

Chris started his Lean journey in 2006 on a public library project in Delray Beach, FL. He is an advocate for Lean processes and IPD and is motivated by the desire to help change the industry and bring more value to project delivery. He has served as a coach for more than 70 project teams across North America.

On a nationwide basis for both internal and external partners, Chris facilitates all-day workshops and training events to help transfer knowledge among professionals who are striving to transform the way projects are designed and built. He is active with Lean Construction Institute (LCI) and regularly speaks at industry events and universities on topics associated with Lean construction and IPD knowledge and practice.

As the Lean/IPD Manager at DPR Construction, Chris collaborates and coordinates with the project team to implement Lean techniques, starting in the design phase of the project and continuing through construction.

His focus includes:

- Developing predictable workflow and deliverables through extensive planning and coordination among all parties

- Building accountability and team confidence among all team members

- Improving subcontractor coordination and performance using Last Planner® System to analyze project failures/breakdowns to establish a continuous-improvement environment

JESSICA **Kelley**

As Director of Learning and Development for Southland Industries, Jessica Kelley draws from her past experiences to grow and refine the organization's learning and development strategy in order to support project execution, team function and Lean thinking.

Jessica started her career with Southland Industries designing and managing lifecycle solutions for large technology, healthcare and biopharmaceutical clients. She has been responsible for successfully delivering projects ranging upwards of $200 million dollars while maintaining budget, schedule, client relationships and design requirements with a focus on value delivery and waste elimination.

For most of Jessica's career in project management, she has focused on Integrated Project Delivery (IPD) projects. She also has worked in project management for an internal role supporting and managing Southland's ERP selection and implementation initiative by applying Lean thinking and tools to internal organizational operations.

In her current role she is able to build on her experiences to support and develop Lean thinking and process application both internally and as a partner to Southland's external IPD project team members.

Jessica has been involved with Lean Construction Institute (LCI), both nationally and at a local level in Northern California, since its inception. She served on the NorCal Community of Practice from 2007 to 2013, holding the Core Group leader role from 2008 through 2012; and served as the 15th Annual LCI Congress Chair. She is a contributing author to the LCI manual Transforming Design and Construction and has been engaged by multiple clients to provide thought leadership on Lean thinking in general and how trade/specialty contractor partners can contribute to the goals of a project.

She also has served on the AGC Training and Education Committee. She continues to remain active in the LCI and Lean construction communities and is an advocate for Lean thinking.

Jessica received her bachelor's degree in architectural engineering with a focus in mechanical from Pennsylvania State University and is a licensed professional engineer in the State of California.

TIMOTHY (TIM) **Klundt**

Timothy (Tim) Klundt is a principal engineer for Corporate Services Construction for Intel Corp. and has more than 30 years of experience in project and design management. He joined Intel in 1994 during a major construction ramp and has held various management roles in Facility and Construction Operations.

In his current role he provides upfront planning for major programs and works with internal customer/stakeholders on capacity-planning solutions. He has been involved with Intel Fabrication Facility planning and design since 1999, managing the design for Intel's first 300mm Fab outside of Oregon; Intel's first 200mm-to-300mm Fab conversion; and eventually managing the Fab Construction Engineering Organization responsible for all major fab conversions, expansions or new builds.

Tim's Lean journey began with Intel's manufacturing organization when a large customer developed Lean techniques to improve process and manufacturing. In 2013 the Construction function within Intel joined the Lean journey and started Intel's internal Lean construction revolution.

Tim was an early adopter of and has facilitated classes on Integrated Project Delivery (IPD) and Target Value Delivery (TVD) to Intel and its major trades.

Prior to joining Intel Tim worked 11 years as a project manager for Morton Thiokol Corp., Utah. He managed the Special Projects group responsible for all new construction projects on the campus, which contained 792 buildings spread over 19,000 acres.

Tim is married to his wife of 34 years and is father to three grown boys. He enjoys family, travel, and a good whiskey and cigar in his leisure time.

DOUGLAS **Lee**

Douglas Lee is Vice President/Regional Preconstruction Director for Brasfield & Gorrie. He manages a department of 40+ estimators in Brasfield & Gorrie's Birmingham, AL, and Nashville, TN, offices. With a passion for integrated project delivery (IPD), Douglas challenges himself, Brasfield & Gorrie, and the IPD teams to learn and improve.

He began his Lean journey in 2007 at the Texoma Medical Center.

As a subject matter expert for Brasfield & Gorrie, Douglas has been featured in Alabama Construction News magazine, speaking as a company subject-matter expert. He has presented at The Walt Disney Co.'s IPD Summit and he has given multiple presentations for Lean Construction Institute (LCI) on Lean project delivery. Douglas is a graduate of Auburn University with a bachelor's degree in Building Science.

He has been married 21 years and is the father of three children.

TAMMY **McConaughy**

Tammy McConaughy is a Senior Lean Specialist with JE Dunn Construction, where she coaches and supports teams using Lean tools such as Target Value Delivery (TVD), Integrated Project Delivery (IPD) and Last Planner® System, along with Lean behaviors.

Tammy began her Lean journey in 2006 in conjunction with the achievement of her Six Sigma Black Belt and has worked in the construction industry since 2003. She has held a supporting role as a Construction Coordinator for a mechanical contractor in the San Diego area, where she worked to learn and apply Lean principles within her organization.

She has been an active participant in multiple Lean Construction Institute (LCI) Communities of Practice and has written and presented for the International Group for Lean Construction. Tammy holds a bachelor's of science degree in Organizational Development from National University.

KATIE **Page**

As Integrated Services Manager for GE Johnson Construction, Katie Page plays an integral role in guiding the company in Integrated Project Delivery (IPD) and Lean practices. ENR Mountain States selected Katie as a 2015 Top 20 Under 40 design and construction professional and an efficiency expert in improvement of job-site processes and technology.

Katie started in the construction industry in 2005, and her Lean journey began in 2007. She has continued to pursue advancement of Lean cultures and practices within her company and the industry. Her Lean advocacy led to a full-time position facilitating and training teams implementing Lean and IPD in 2014.

She currently is working on multiple IPD projects for healthcare and advanced-technology clients.

In 2010 Katie partnered with three colleagues to establish the Lean Construction Institute (LCI) Colorado Community of Practice, which today has more than 400 members.

As a Core Group member, Katie provides overall direction for the group through educational events and speaking engagements. Training industry practitioners has earned Katie a reputation as a mentor and leader.

She graduated from Duke University with a bachelor's of science in Civil/Structural Engineering and Certificate in Architectural Engineering in 2005.

STACEY **Root**

Stacey Root joined Boulder Associates in 2008 and worked on a Sutter Health Integrated Project Delivery (IPD) team. After this introduction to true collaboration and Lean thinking, Stacey became a designated in-house Lean evangelist. Informed by her background playing soccer, she knows the value of bringing different skillsets together working toward a common goal, and this translates to building design and construction. She loves collaborating directly with end-users, and since 2010 Stacey has facilitated more than a dozen weeklong 3P events.

Every summer, Stacey rides her bicycle across the state of Iowa.

WILLIAM **R. (Bill) Seed**

Bill Seed is a Senior Executive Consultant who empowers project teams to achieve predictable outcomes in a reduced-stress project environment. As a Transformational Achiever Coach, he uses his owner's leadership experience to develop teams that complete projects consistently on time and under budget.

He has spent over 30 years in the construction related industry, 23 years specifically dedicated to health care mostly in an owner representative role. He helped Walt Disney Imagineering introduce a new project delivery model of Integrated Project Delivery for numerous projects. He earned his Bachelor of Science in

Mechanical Engineering from the University of Akron, Ohio in 1990.

Bill has had responsibility in overseeing $3Billion of construction and design activities for Universal Health Services, Inc. He and his various teams have developed over 2000 new Behavioral Health beds including 4 green field campuses, 5 new Medical Acute Care hospitals, and numerous large and smaller facility enhancements. Many of these projects utilized IPD methods and contracts and have shown phenomenal results.

He is a member of National Academy of Constructors, Chairman of the Board of Directors of the Lean Construction Institute, the winner of the LCI Pioneer award in 2012, and an active owner advocate for the implementation of Integrated Lean Project Delivery.

RYAN Seckinger

Ryan Seckinger is a Principal at Walter P Moore and has more than 15 years of structural engineering and team management experience. He leads the firm's Integrated Project Delivery (IPD) initiatives and is committed to leveraging collaborative working relationships, innovative technology, and intentional Lean practices to enable best-for-project solutions.

Specializing in large, complex projects, Ryan has a particular interest in improving the way integrated teams apply Lean principles and design thinking to rebuild the project delivery process.

ROBERT Shmerling

Robert Shmerling is a Project Design Management Executive at Walt Disney Imagineering, leading project teams in the development of large-scale, complex themed-entertainment projects. Robert has developed Lean strategies for multiple projects since 2008, following them through all phases of design and implementation.

This includes executive leadership of Disney's first Integrated Project Delivery (IPD) project in the theme park, and presentation of this work, Collaborative Design of Unique, Large Scale Thematic Structures, at the 17th Annual Lean Construction Institute (LCI) Congress; as well as the P2SL-LCI-AIA Lean Design Forum 2016.

He is a licensed engineer and received his bachelor's degree from the University of California, Berkeley, and master's degree from the University of Central Florida; as well as certifications from Stanford University in Virtual Design and Construction, and the Harvard Graduate School of Design in architecture and urban design.

REBECCA **Snelling**

Rebecca Snelling coaches a variety of people, teams and organizations on Lean transformation. Currently she coaches on Lean leadership while developing and leading a group of coaches and trainers for all employees and project teams implementing Last PlannerÐ System in design and construction; Target Value Design (TVD); Integrated Project Delivery (IPD); Choosing By Advantages (CBA); and other Lean practices and behaviors.

She started in the construction industry in 1996, beginning her Lean journey in 2006, and is currently employed by JE Dunn Construction as their National Lean Director.

Prior to JE Dunn, Rebecca spent more than five years consulting on the application of Lean principles in various organizations and project types. This includes working with owners, designers, builders and engineers, Integrated Project Delivery (IPD) teams, leading strategic planning sessions and implementing various other Lean practices. Rebecca has developed and delivered training materials and written white papers on various Lean Construction applications. She has been actively involved with the Lean Construction Institute (LCI) and is a contributing author of the LCI manual Transforming Design and Construction, a Framework for Change. She speaks at various industry events across the country and abroad.

Rebecca is the Chair of the LCI Education Committee, an LCI Improved Instructor, and also a Master Trainer of the Choosing by Advantages Decision-making System. Rebecca holds a degree in business management from the University of Phoenix.

MARK **Spies**

Mark Spies is a Principal at Stengel Hill Architecture (SHA) based in Louisville, KY. Mark began his career at SHA in 2002 after graduating with a bachelor's of Architecture from the University of Cincinnati.

As a Principal, Mark is heavily involved in all aspects of the firm from planning and design to business development to ensure the continued growth and success of SHA as it approaches its 20th anniversary.

Mark began his Lean journey in 2010 and continues to grow with each Integrated Project Delivery (IPD)/Lean project he is involved in throughout the country.

Contributors, facilitators and support team members at collaborative session for planning and writing this manual at JE Dunn Construction, Denver, Colo.

APPENDICES

Glossary

Kickoff Workshop Agenda Example

References

Ordering Information for More Books

About the Lean Construction Institute

GLOSSARY

A3

A one-page report prepared on a single 11-by-17-inch sheet of paper that adheres to the discipline of PDCA thinking as applied to problem-solving – or A3 thinking. The A3 includes the background, problem statement, analysis, proposed corrective actions (and action plan), and the expected results, often with graphics.

Allowable Cost (AC)

What an owner is willing and able to pay in order to get what they want; i.e., what that product or asset is worth to them.

Big Room (Oba, Obeeya)

Physical space where multidisciplinary specialists can meet to share incomplete information, collaborate and maintain a visual workplace.

BIM, see Building Information Model(-ing).

Building Information Model(-ing) (BIM)

The process of generating and managing building data during the life cycle of a building. BIM uses three-dimensional (3-D), real-time, dynamic building modeling software. BIM includes building geometry, spatial relationships, geographic information, and quantities and properties of building components. BIM can include four-dimensional (4-D) simulations to see how part or all of the facility is intended to be built and 5-D capability for model-based estimating. BIM provides the platform for simultaneous conversations related to the design of the "product" and its delivery process..

Choosing by Advantages (CBA)

CBA is a tested and effective sound decision-making system developed by Jim Suhr (1999) for determining the best decision by looking at the advantages of each option. CBA's five phases of decision-making:

1. Stage-setting: establish the purpose and context for the decision;

2. Innovation: formulate an adequate set of alternatives;

3. Decision-making: choose the alternative with the greatest total importance of advantages;

4. Reconsideration: change the decision if it should be changed or improved on; and

5. Implementation: make the decision happen, adjust as needed, and evaluate the process and results.

Conditions of Satisfaction (COS)

An explicit description by a customer of all the actual requirements that must be satisfied by the performer in order for the customer to feel that they received exactly what was wanted.

Constraint

Something that stands in the way of a task being executable or sound. Typical constraints on design tasks are inputs from others, clarity of requirements criteria for what is to be produced or provided, approvals or releases, and labor or equipment resources. Typical constraints on construction tasks are the completion of design or prerequisite work; availability of materials, information and directives. Screening tasks for readiness is assessing the status of their constraints. Removing constraints is making a task ready to be assigned.

Cost Modeling

Developing a model of the cost components and systems specific to a project and structuring it in a manner that the components and system costs can be continually updated either via benchmarks, metrics or detailed estimated to provide the team with a constantly up to date cost model for the project. In the TVD environment, the cost model should allow for projecting 'what-if' scenarios based on value decisions that have yet to be made.

Customer

The individual engaged in a conversation for action who will receive the results of performance either requested from, or offered by, the Performer. I.e. – the person receiving goods/information from a performer. Customers can be internal (a foreman receiving answer to an RFI, Architect receiving mechanical loads from engineer), and external (end users, client organizations, etc).

Design

A type of goal-directed, reductive (not deductive) reasoning. There are always many possible designs, especially if one is willing to relax constraints (requirements). Product design reasons from function to form. Process design reasons from ends to means.

EC, see Expected Cost

Expected Cost (EC)

An expression of the best estimate at the conclusion of the Validation Phase of what current best practice would produce as a price for the facility reflected in the accompanying basis of design documents. Typically, the Expected Cost also will be supported by benchmarking or other market data to calibrate the Expected Cost in light of the market context.

First-Run Study (FRS)

Trial execution of a process in order to determine the best means, methods, sequencing, etc. to perform it. A FRS follows the Plan-Do-Check-Act cycle. First-run studies are done at least a few weeks ahead of the scheduled execution of the process, while there is time to acquire different or additional prerequisites and resources. They may also be performed during design as a basis for evaluating options or designing the portion of the work.

Integrated Project Delivery™ (IPD):

A project delivery approach that integrates people, systems, business structures and practices into a process that collaboratively harnesses the talents and insights of all participants to reduce waste and optimize efficiency through all phases of the project, from early design through project handover. The three contractual components of IPD include Organization structure, Lean Operating Systems and Commercial Terms.

Last Planner® System (LPS)

System for project production planning and control, aimed at creating a workflow that achieves reliable execution, developed by Glenn Ballard and Greg Howell, with documentation by Ballard in 2000. LPS is the collaborative, commitment-based planning system that integrates should-can-will-did planning: pull planning, make-ready look-ahead planning with constraint analysis, weekly work planning based upon reliable promises, and learning based upon analysis of PPC and Reasons for Variance.

Last Responsible Moment (LRM)

The instant in which the cost of the delay of a decision surpasses the benefit of delay; or the moment when failing to take a decision eliminates an important alternative.

LPS, see Last Planner System

LRM, see Last Responsible Moment

Market Cost (MC)

What an owner may expect to pay for a desired asset based on comparison with historical market cost for similar assets. Hence, it is the initial expected cost determined through benchmarking to market of the owner's wants. The comparison with allowable cost determines whether or not to proceed with validation. It comes into play in business planning or in the course of the budget validation.

Oba, Obeeya, see Big Room

Percent Plan Complete (PPC)

A basic measure of how well the planning system is working - calculated as the "number of promises/activities completed on the day stated" divided by the "total number of promises/activities made/planned for the week". It measures the percentage of assignments that are 100% complete as planned.

Plan, Do, Check, Act (PDCA)

According to the Lean Enterprise Institute: PDCA is an improvement cycle based on the scientific method of proposing a change in a process, measuring the results and taking appropriate action.

The PDCA cycle has four stages:

Plan: Determining goals for a process and needed changes to achieve them

Do: Implement the change

Check: Evaluate the results in terms of performance

Act: Standardize and stabilize the change or begin the cycle again, depending on results.

Plus/Delta

A discussion at the end of an activity, meeting or project used to evaluate and learn from its performance by capturing: (1) pluses: What worked or produced value during the session? and (2) deltas: What could we do differently or better next time to improve the process or outcome?

Point-Based Design (PBD)

A design methodology whereby one (or a few alternative) solutions to parts of the problem may be explored, one gets selected, and that one is then passed on to the next design specialist.

PPC, see Percent Plan Complete

Pull Planning

A method of advancing work when the next in line customer is ready to use it. A "Request" from the customer signals that the work is needed and is "pulled" from the performer. Pull releases work when the system is ready to use it.

Set-Based Design (SBD)

A design method whereby sets of alternative solutions to parts of the problem are kept open until their Last Responsible Moment(s), in order to find by means of set intersection the best combination that solves the problem as a whole.

TA, see Tasks Anticipated

Target Cost (TC)

The cost that a project team is striving to achieve, either less than or equal to the allowable cost, and typically a stretch goal relative to previous performance capability. Note that the project target may be set in terms of scope: to deliver more value for a given cost. The Target Cost should be set at less than best-in-class past performance. The goal is to create a sense of necessity to drive innovation and waste reduction into the design and construction process.

Target Costing

A method used by consumer and industrial product manufacturers to manage product profitability (Cooper & Slagmulder 1997 and 1999). After defining the functionalities of a new product and conducting market studies, the manufacturer estimates the revenues it will receive from sales, subtracts the profit considered acceptable, and the remainder is the target cost—the most money the manufacturer can spend on designing, manufacturing, servicing and disposing of the product and still make its target profit.

Target Value Design (TVD)

Encompasses the Target Value Delivery approaches implemented during the design delivery phases of the project.

Target Value Delivery (TVD)

A disciplined management practice to be used throughout the project to assure that the facility meets the operational needs and values of the users, is delivered within the allowable budget, and promotes innovation throughout the process to increase value and eliminate waste (time, money, human effort.)

Target Value Production

Encompasses the Target Value Delivery approaches implemented during the construction delivery phases of the project.

Tasks Anticipated (TA)

A metric in the Last Planner® System that gauges the percentage of all tasks in a plan for a target week that were anticipated in an earlier plan for that target week. Together with Tasks Made Ready (TMR), it characterizes the ability of the planning team to make work ready.

Tasks Made Ready (TMR)

Metric in the Last Planner® System that gauges the percentage of tasks in an earlier plan for a target week that are included in a later plan for the target week. Together with Tasks Anticipated (TA) it characterizes the ability of the planning team to make work ready.

TMR, see Tasks Made Ready

TVD, see Target Value Design

Value

What the Customer wants from the process. The customer defines value.

Values

Behavioral principles, rules for how people should behave. Expressed as conditions of satisfaction or constraints on the selection of ends and means.

Virtual First Run Study (VFRS)

Virtual prototyping effort conducted well in advance of the execution of the work being studied, in order to learn how it can be done in the best possible way.

Virtual Prototyping

Developing models in a computer system, such as a BIM, to study the design and production of a product or process.

Whole Life Target Value Delivery, see Target Value Design

Worth

Assessment of costs and benefits from use of the asset to be constructed (asset worth).

KICK OFF WORKSHOP
AGENDA EXAMPLE

Kickoff Onboarding Workshop	Day 1
LEAN CONSTRUCTION INTRODUCTION	
Ice breaker Question and or Activity	
Lean Construction Introduction	
Break	
Continue with Lean Introduction, Make-a-Card simulation	
Lunch	
High-Performance Teaming: • What's working, what's not?	
Break	
Development of Values Matrix • Understanding interplay between goals and values • Breakout sessions to develop 3 important values on project • Report back • Develop specific values against which all project decisions will be made	
Plus/Delta	
Adjournment	
Team Building Activity: Dinner/Happy Hour, etc.	

VALUES WORKSHOP ACTIVITY

Ice breaker Question and or Activity
Values Matrix, continued
• Craft final values
Break
Team Goals Discussion
• Develop goals, governing factors and metrics for important success measures, including: LEED, lighting levels, flexibility, reduced and reliable delivery time • Review goals against values
Report back on Goals development • Big Room Discussion on winnowing/crafting goals
Lunch
Silent Squares Collaboration Simulation
Team Dynamics
• Co-location • Virtual communication for teaming • Tools • Management
Additional Team Members • MEP and other important trades • Integration strategy as we add trades
Break
Team Composition and Management

• Sr. Management Team
• Project Management Team
• Integrated Team
   • Empowering team members to work at their horizontal competence level
   • Issue elevation and resolution process
      • Executive
      • Program Management
      • Field Teams

Communication Protocol
• How SMT and Core Team members communicate daily, weekly, etc. • Creation of A3 reporting and decision making template
Plus Delta
Adjournment

Kickoff Onboarding Workshop

Day 3

TEAM BUILDING/STRUCTURE/PROTOCOL

Target Value Design

How do we use trade partners in design assistance and enable design of delivery for later integrated trades?
- Clusters—cross organizational teams
- Set Based Design
- Collaboration on Teams
- Breakouts in Clusters
- Begin Budget breakdown

Break

Report backs

Responsibility/delivery Matrix
- Establish deliverables

Lunch

Milestone Pull
- Establish timing for next steps and deliverables

BIM protocols and technology platforms

Break
- Reimbursement models
- Risk and reward
  - Develop incentive compensation model
  - Decide who's in the circle

Path Forward

Plus/Delta

Adjournment

REFERENCES

AIA National; AIA California Council, "Integrated Project Delivery, A Guide," 2007

AIA California Conference, "Integrated Project Delivery, A Working Definition," 2007

Ask, Julie A.; Laseter, Tim, "Cost Modeling: A Foundation Purchasing Skill," strategy+business, Q1 1998

Bade, Michael; Haas, Christine, "Mission Bay Block 25 Building: An Exercise in Target Value Design," from proceedings for the Lean in Public Sector Construction Conference, 2014

Ballard, Glenn, "Positive Vs. Negative Iteration in Design," 2000

Ballard, Glenn, "The Last Planner® System of Production Control," The University of Birmingham, 2000

Ballard, Glenn, "Managing work flow on design projects: a case study," Engineering, Construction and Architectural Management, Vol. 9 Issue 3, pp. 284-291

Ballard, Glenn, "The Lean Project Delivery System: An Update," Lean Construction Journal, 2008

Ballard, Glenn, "Process Benchmarks: Target Value Design: Current Benchmark (1.0)," Lean Construction Journal, 2011

Ballard, Glenn, "Should Project Budgets Be Based on Worth or Cost?" from proceedings for the 20th Annual Conference of the International Group for Lean Construction

Dal Gallo, Lisa; O'Leary, Shawn T.; Louridas, Laila Jadelrab, "Comparison of Integrated Project Delivery Agreements," Hanson Bridgett LLP

Denerolle, Stéphane, "Technical Report: The application of Target Value Design to the design phase of 3 hospital projects," Project Production Systems Laboratory, University of California, Berkeley, June 2011

Ferry, Brandon, pp. 113-114, Cost Planning of Buildings, 1984

Gupta, Arjun P.; Tommelein, Iris D.; Blume, Katherine, "Framework for Using A3s to Develop Shared Understanding of Projects," from proceedings for the 17th Annual Conference of the International Group for Lean Construction

Knott, Terry, No Business As Usual: Improving the performance of capital project, ISBN 0 86165 202 9

Lee, Hyun Woo; Tommelein, Iris D.; Ballard, Glenn, "Design of an Infrastructure Project Using a Point-Based Methodology," ASCE, Journal of Management and Engineering, July 2012

Lichtig, William A., "The Integrated Agreement for Lean Project Delivery," ABA, Construction Lawyer, Summer 2006

Macomber, Hal; Barberio, John, "Target-Value Design: Nine Foundational Practices for Delivering Surprising Client Value," Lean Project Consulting

Macomber, Hal; Howell, Greg; Barberio, John, "Target-Value Design: Nine Foundational and Six Advanced Practices For Delivering Surprising Client Value," Lean Project Consulting, 2012

Markovitz, Daniel, "The Folly of Stretch Goals," Harvard Business Review, April 2012

Matthews, Owen; Howell, Gregory A.; Mitropoulos, Panagiotis, "Aligning the Lean Organization: A Contractual Approach," 2003

Matthews, Owen; Howell, Gregory A., "Integrated Project Delivery An Example of Relational Contracting," 2005

Morton, Scott; Ballard, Glenn, "Conceptual Estimating in Project Capital Planning and Validation", 2009

Nguyen, Hung Viet, "Process-Based Cost Modeling to Support Target Value Design," 2012

Seed, William R. (Bill), "Last Planners Construction Phase: Onboarding Presentation," Temecula Valley Hospital, May 2016

Seed, William R. (Bill), "Integrated Project Delivery Requires a New Project Manager," 2014

Shook, John, "Toyota's Secret: The A3 Report," Sloan Management Review, Summer 2009

Ward, Allen; Liker, Jeffrey K.; Cristiano, John J.; Sobek, Durward K. II, "The Second Toyota Paradox: How Delaying Decisions Can Make Better Cars Faster," Sloan Management Review, Spring 1995

ORDER ADDITIONAL COPIES

For additional copies of this publication, please contact Julia Shellhouse, LCI Administration Manager: jshellhouse@leanconstruction.org or 703-387-3050.

Unit price: $45

LCI Corporate Member discounts available.

We Invite You to Join LCI

We cordially invite your firm to join us in the movement to transform design and construction through the concepts, tools and techniques of Lean project design and delivery. Lean can benefit your organization and personnel whether you are an owner organization, a contractor, a design firm, or one of the skilled trades. Through our regional Communities of Practice, events, the website, and other benefits such as all-expense paid training for new corporate members, we are working to transform our industry by making a difference. In short, supporting and participating in LCI provides corporate member companies with the foundation for a sustainable competitive advantage.

For more information on LCI membership, please contact Ilene Goldberg, LCI Manager of Membership and CoP Relations: **igoldberg@leanconstruction.org** or **703-387-3049**.

For more information on Lean Construction Institute, visit **www.leanconstruction.org**

Lean Construction Institute
1400 N. 14th Street, 12th Floor
Arlington, VA 22209

LEAN CONSTRUCTION INSTITUTE

Lean Construction Institute (LCI) is a non-profit organization, founded in 1997. The Institute operates as a catalyst to transform the industry through Lean project delivery using an operating system centered on a common language, fundamental principles, and basic practices.

With over 180 corporate members, representing the Owner, Designer, General Contractor and Trade Partner communities, LCI is a voice for industry transformation. LCI sponsors programs to assist members on all stages of their Lean journey.

LCI Vision:
Transform the Design and Construction Industry supply chain to provide value and enable other industries through Lean and integrated approaches.

LCI Mission:
The mission of LCI is to transform Design and Construction through new approaches to project design and delivery. Lean theory, principles and techniques, taken together, provide the foundation for a different, more collaborative, and more effective form of project management. Lean Design and Construction represents a transformational way to design and build capital facilities. The Lean approach generates significant improvements in schedule with dramatically reduced waste, particularly on complex, uncertain and quick projects.

Goals:
Increase owner and construction supply chain satisfaction with design and construction delivery.

- Deliver Standard Building Blocks for Lean and Integrated Delivery
- Create Construction Industry Demand & Capacity for Lean & Integrated Approaches
- Achieve Customer Value while Eliminating Waste throughout Project Life Cycle
- Achieve Supply Chain Partner Value while Eliminating Waste throughout Project Life Cycle
- Create a Vibrant Learning Environment across the Country to share Best Practices

For more information on Lean Construction Institute, visit www.leanconstruction.org
Lean Construction Institute, 1400 N. 14th Street, 12th Floor, Arlington, VA 22209